D1622354

SRA

BUILDING
Vocabulary
Skills

Level 3
Student Edition

Columbus, OH • Chicago, IL • Redmond, WA

The **McGraw·Hill** Companies

www.sra4kids.com

 SRA

Copyright © 2003 by SRA/McGraw-Hill.

Send all inquiries to:
SRA/McGraw-Hill
4400 Easton Commons
Columbus, OH 43219

Printed in the United States of America.

ISBN 0-07-579614-7

10 11 12 13 14 QPD 09 08

The **McGraw·Hill** Companies

Table of Contents

Unit 3

Unit 4

Vocabulary List

1. **companion**
   (kəm pan′ yən) *n.*
   friend

2. **devotion** *sùng bái, hâm mộ*
   (di vō′ shən) *n.*
   strong attachment; *lòng huyến ái , cantuđ*
   love

3. **thoughtful**
   (thôt′ fəl) *adj.*
   kind; thinking of
   others

4. **loyal**
   (loi′ əl) *adj.*
   faithful

5. **mutual** *chung*
   (mū′ choo əl) *adj.* *hổ tương*
   something shared

6. **keen** *, bén, as keen as razor*
   (kēn) *adj.* *bén như dao cạo*
   strongly interested in *cuộc đua háo nức* *keen competitos*

7. **regard**
   (ri gärd′) *n.*
   respect

8. **precious** *quí giá*
   (presh′ əs) *adj.* *my precious*
   valuable *con yêu qui của tôi*

9. **upright** *ngbinh , vôtu*
   (up′ rīt) *adj.*
   good; honest

10. **confide** *tin cậy ,*
    (kən fīd′) *v.*
    to tell as a secret *giải bày tâm sự*

confidence : lòng tin ,
chuyện tò mật , tâm sự

"Friendship" Vocabulary

 **1** **Word Meanings**

Words in Context

 Write the word that fits best in each blank.
Each word is used only once.

1. If you _____confide_____ in someone, make
   sure that you can trust him or her not to tell your
   secrets to others.

2. George Washington was an _____upright_____
   young man who answered questions honestly.

3. John Adams and Thomas Jefferson had a strong

   respect, or _____regard_____, for each other.

4. Sending a thank-you note for a gift is a

   _____thoughtful_____, or kind, thing to do.

5. A _____precious_____ object, such as a diamond
   ring, is something that you value highly and don't
   want to lose.

6. A strong love, or _____devotion_____, is what
   kept Abigail and John Adams married for 54 years.

7. Winnie the Pooh is Christopher Robin's famous

   _____companion_____, or pal.

8. If you're not really _____keen_____ about
   listening to piano music, perhaps jazz will interest
   you more.

9. When two people make a _____mutual_____
   decision, they share in the decision-making process.

10. A _____loyal_____ pet is faithful to its
    owner.

② Reference Skills

Dictionary Entries

 Answer each question about the dictionary entries for the vocabulary words that are shown in the box below.

> **confide** (kən fīd′) *v.* **1.** to tell as a secret; entrust.
>
> **keen** (kēn) *adj.* **1.** very strong; intense. **2.** having or showing great mental sharpness.
>
> **regard** (ri gärd′) *n.* **1.** respect or affection.
> –*v.* **2.** to show respect or consideration for.

1. Which word can be used as either a noun or a verb?

   _____ regard _____

2. Which word has only one syllable?

   _____ keen _____

3. Which words have more than one definition?

   _____ keen , regard _____

4. Write the definition of *keen* that is shown in the sentence below.

   Because he was so smart, people said he had a keen

   mind. __having great mental sharpness.__

   _____

5. Write the definition of *keen* that is shown in the sentence below.

   Mrs. Edge has a keen interest in French paintings.

   __intense / very strong.__

Vocabulary List

1. companion
2. devotion
3. thoughtful
4. loyal
5. mutual hỗ trợ
6. keen
7. regard
8. precious
9. upright
10. confide

3 Build New Vocabulary

Suffixes -less and -ful

The suffix -less means "without or lacking."
The suffix -ful means "full of."

Change the suffix in each boldfaced word to -less. Write the new word in the blank.

1. The opposite of **thoughtful** is

    thoughtless.

2. The opposite of **harmful** is

    harmless (bình an)

3. The opposite of **painful** is

    painless.

4. The opposite of **restful** is

   restless (ở nghĩ, ở sự vữ dộng)

• •

Draw a line to match each word to its definition.

5. thoughtless   **A.** dangerous; full of harm

6. painful   **B.** not able to rest

7. restless   **C.** not thinking of others

8. harmless   **D.** full of pain

9. thoughtful   **E.** lacking harm; safe

10. harmful   **F.** caring about others

4 Word Play

Similes   sự so sánh, đối chiếu)

A **simile** uses ~~like~~ or ~~as~~ to compare two things that are not alike. In the example below, two friends are being compared to peas that grow together in a pod: → vỏ (đậu) vỏ (trứng)

Brad and Jorge are such close friends that they are like two peas in a pod.

 Complete each simile with the vocabulary word that makes the most sense. Then write the two things that are being compared.

1. My friends are as _precious_ to me as gold.

   (My _friends_ are being compared to _gold_ because they are highly valuable.)

2. Our soccer fans are as _loyal_ to our team as dogs are to their masters. (Soccer _fans_ are being compared to _dogs_ because they are faithful.)

3. I take my CD player with me so often that it is just like a _companion_. (A person's CD _player_ is being compared to a _companion_ because it is as constant as a friend.)

4. The two enemies have as much _____ for each other as cats do for mice. (Two _enemies_ are being compared to _cats_ and _mice_ who do not respect each other.)

Unit 1
Lesson 2

Vocabulary List

1. **humble** *tầm thường, thấp kém*
   (hum' bəl) *adj.*
   not proud

2. **amusing**
   (ə mūz' ing) *adj.*
   entertaining

3. **frank** *chân thật*
   (frangk) *adj.*
   honest and
   outspoken

4. **clever**
   (klev' ər) *adj.*
   alert and quick

5. **miserable**
   (miz' ər ə bəl) *adj.*
   very unhappy

6. **open-minded**
   (ō' pən mīn' did)
   adj. ready to think
   about new ideas

7. **noble**
   (nō' bəl) *adj.*
   fair and honorable

8. **genius**
   (jēn' yəs) *n.*
   a gifted person

9. **sensitive**
   (sen' si tiv) *adj.*
   hiểu biết aware of others'
   feelings

10. **reliable**
    (ri lī' ə bəl) *adj.*
    able to be trusted

Describing People

1 Word Meanings

Examples

 Write the vocabulary word that fits each example.

1. A person standing in freezing rain _genius_

2. A person who is always ready to try new things
   open-minded

3. A person who began writing music at age three
   noble

4. A person who speaks up to give her opinion
   frank

5. A person who hugs her friend when he's feeling sad
   miserable

6. A mail carrier who delivers the mail from Monday to
   Saturday _humble_

7. A person who returns a wallet filled with money to its
   owner _frank_

8. An actor on TV who makes people want to watch his
   show _sensitive_

9. A person who can add a list of numbers in his head
   clever

10. A really good soccer player who never brags _khoe_
    khoang
    reliable

6   Unit 1 • Lesson 2   Score _____ (Top Score 10)   Describing People • Word Meanings

② Reference Skills
Pronunciation Symbols

Each phonetic spelling stands for a word or words that rhyme with part of or all of a Vocabulary List word. Choose the vocabulary word that <u>rhymes</u> with each phonetic spelling and write it in the blank.

vần, vận   sự hợp vần

/a/, **at**; /ā/, **late**; /ȧ/, **care**; /ä/, **father**; /e/, **set**; /ē/, **me**;
/i/, **it**; /ī/, **kite**; /o/, **ox**; /ō/, **rose**; /ô/, **brought, raw**; /oi/,
coin; /o͝o/, **book**; /o͞o/, **too**; /or/, **form**; /ou/, **out**; /u/, **up**;
/yo͞o/, **cube**; /ûr/, **turn, germ, learn, firm, work**; /ə/, **about**,
chicken, pencil, cannon, circus; /ch/, **chair**; /hw/, **which**;
/ng/, **ring**; /sh/, **shop**; /th/, **thin**; /th/, **there**; /zh/, **treasure**

1. mō´ bəl   _____

2. ə plī´ ə bəl   _____apliable_____

3. dangk   _____

4. vē´ nəs   _____venus_____

5. kən fū´ zing   _____confusing_____

6. nev´ ər   _____never_____

7. res´t iv   _____restive_____

8. tō´ kən/spī/kid   _____

9. viz´ ə bəl   _____veserble_____

10. fum´ bəl   _____

Vocabulary List

1. humble

2. amusing

3. frank

4. clever

5. miserable

6. open-minded

7. noble

8. genius

9. sensitive

10. reliable

frank (v) hả phưởg tiến tên cưới fi!
(a) : thành thật, chaithtm

3 Build New Vocabulary
The Suffix -ness

Add the suffix *-ness* to the words below. Write the new word in the blank.

1. frank _____frankness_____

2. thoughtful _____thoughtfulness_____

3. precious _____preciousness_____

4. open-minded _____open-mindedness_____

5. clever _____cleverness_____

Complete each sentence below using one of the new words that you made above.

6. The _____preciousness_____ of a true friend is greater than the value of gold.

7. People who are quick to answer hard questions have _____cleverness_____.

8. Thinking about other people's ideas and accepting differences among people shows great _____open-mindedness_____.

9. When my mother asks me to explain why I've done something wrong, she expects complete _____frankness_____ from me.

10. I was thankful for my mother's _____thoughtfulness_____ when she made my favorite dinner on my birthday.

Word Play

Exaggerations   sự quá đáng, hùng đại

 Each sentence below makes something sound much greater than it really is. Complete each sentence with the vocabulary word that makes the most sense.

1. The speaker is so _____ that she can answer any question you ask her without even stopping to think.

2. The actors in the movie were so

   _____ that we couldn't stop laughing for a week.

3. Grandpa is so _____ that the sun calls him on the phone every morning to find out what time it is.

4. I feel so _____ that I'm going to shut myself up for a year and cry my eyes out.

5. The captain of our team is so

   _____ that she calls the president of the United States to tell him what she thinks about his decisions.

6. My sister is so _____ that she knows how people feel before they know themselves.

7. That test was so hard that you'd have to be a

   _____ just to understand the questions.

8. Our neighbor is so _____ that she has a window in the back of her head.

Vocabulary List

1. **associate**
(ə sō′ shē āt) *v.*
to be friendly with

2. **harmony**
här′ mə nē) *n.*
agreement

3. **cooperate**
(kō op ə rāt′) *v.*
to work well with
others

4. **suggestion**
(səg jes′ chən) *n.*
an idea that is
offered

5. **ignore**
(ig nor′) *v.*
to pay no attention to

6. **judge**
(juj) *v.*
to form an opinion

7. **reasonable**
(rē′ zə nə bəl) *adj.*
having good sense

8. **consent**
(kən sent′) *v.*
to say yes; agree to

9. **settle**
(set′ əl) *v.*
to decide on

10. **interaction**
(in tə rak′ shən) *n.*
action between two
people

Getting Along

① Word Meanings

Definitions

 Write the vocabulary word that correctly
completes each sentence.

1. When people agree in a pleasant way about

   something, they are all in _____
   with one another.

2. When something is fair and makes sense, we say that

   it is _____.

3. To _____ on something is to make
   a firm decision about it.

4. When you _____ to something,
   you are giving permission, or saying 'yes.'

5. When you form an opinion about something, you

   _____ it.

6. An action between two or more people is called an

   _____.

7. When you spend time with your friends, you

   _____ with them.

8. An idea that someone offers about something is a
   ___*suggestion*___.

9. To _____ something is to take no
   notice of it.

10. When people work well together for a common goal,

    they_____ with one another.

2 Reference Skills

Guide Words

 For each word below, decide whether the word would be found on the same dictionary page as the guide words next to it. Write Yes or No to show your answer.

1. consent   civil/crate   _____

2. settle   scratch/shock   _____

3. harmony   heard/helpful   _____

4. associate   attend/audio   _____

5. cooperation   clearly/crunch   _____

6. ignore   ideal/illegal   _____

7. interaction   imperfect/iron   _____

8. judge   joke/joyful   _____

9. reasonable   radiate/ringside   _____

10. suggestion   sorely/speck   _____

 Write the following words in alphabetical order: interaction, judge, associate, ignore, harmony.

11. _____

12. _____

13. _____

14. _____

15. _____

Vocabulary List

1. *associate*

2. *harmony*

3. *cooperate*

4. *suggestion*

5. *ignore*

6. *judge*

7. *reasonable*

8. *consent*

9. *settle*

10. *interaction*

3 Build New Vocabulary

Context Clues: Contrast

 Complete each sentence in the passage below using one of the vocabulary words. The underlined words in each sentence have the *opposite* meaning of the word that correctly completes each sentence.

The American Colonies Go to War with England in 1776

1. The American colonists wanted their opinions <u>to be considered</u> by the English government, but the king

   of England had chosen to _____ them instead.

2. King George created <u>disorder</u> by treating the colonists

   unjustly and he destroyed any _____ between England and the colonists.

3. Many colonists did not think it was

   _____ for a king to rule them—they thought the idea <u>made no sense</u>. Instead, they wanted to choose their leaders.

4. The two sides <u>could not agree</u>, so they could not

   _____ their differences.

5. After the war began, many colonists <u>wanted to have nothing to do with</u> the people who were on England's

   side, so they would not _____ with them.

6. George Washington decided to _____ to lead the new American army; however, after the war had been won, <u>he said that he would not</u> continue to lead.

Word Play

Alliteration

 Write the vocabulary word that completes each example of alliteration below.

1. Sally made a silly _____ about the song that the singers should sing.

2. Jenny's job was just to _____ the juice and the jelly.

3. I intended to go inside to see the interesting

   _____ indoors.

4. Rosa really realizes that the rules are

   _____.

5. The cooking crew could clearly

   _____ to create creamy cakes, but the clean-up crowd caused chaos.

6. I suppose we should soon _____ on a sound solution.

7. Iggy indicated that I had to _____ the insects in India.

8. I can't _____ to Cholena's crazy conditions.

9. Have you heard the heavenly _____ of her harp and his harmonica?

10. Ahmed always allows all the apes to

    _____ with one another.

1. **destruction**
   (di struk´ shən) n.
   the act of breaking
   or ruining

2. **division**
   (di vizh´ ən) n.
   the act of dividing
   or splitting

3. **complain**
   (kəm plān´) v.
   to talk about faults

4. **debate**
   (di bāt´) n.
   a discussion or
   argument

5. **disturb**
   (di stûrb´) v.
   to bother or upset

6. **resist**
   (re zist´) v.
   to not give in to

7. **oppose**
   (op ōz´) v.
   to be against

8. **unpleasant**
   (un plez´ ənt) adj.
   not enjoyable,
   not nice

9. **object**
   (əb jekt´) v.
   to say no

10. **neutral**
    (noo´ trəl) adj.
    not taking sides

Vocabulary for Conflict

1 Word Meanings

Antonyms

Read each sentence below. Write the vocabulary word that means the opposite of the underlined word or words.

1. Habitat for Humanity is a group of volunteers that help families with the <u>construction</u> of their homes.

   _____

2. The families must <u>consent</u> to help build their homes but usually this does not disturb them.

   _____

3. They soon find that the job of building a home is <u>enjoyable</u>. _____

4. The volunteers first reach an <u>agreement</u> about the plan for the house. _____

5. One of the volunteers might remain neutral and help bring about a <u>union</u> of ideas.

   _____

6. A volunteer who disagrees with the others about the plan will usually <u>give in</u> and accept their idea.

   _____

7. The families usually <u>support</u> the volunteers' final plan and they work together in harmony.

   _____

8. The families <u>praise</u> the volunteers for their hard work. _____

② Reference Skills

Alphabetical Order

dentist	debate
division	destruction
discover	devote
disturb	determine
demand	dinners

 Write the words from the box above in alphabetical order in the blanks below. Then unscramble the boxed letters to spell the answer to the question at the bottom of the page.

1. ☐ _ _ _ _ _ _

2. _ _ _ _ ☐ _

3. _ _ _ _ _ ☐ _

4. _ _ _ _ _ ☐ _ _ _ _

5. _ _ _ _ _ _ ☐ _ _ _

6. _ _ _ ☐ _ _

7. _ _ _ _ _ ☐

8. _ ☐ _ _ _ _ _

9. _ _ _ _ ☐ _ _

10. _ _ _ _ ☐ _ _ _

A good way for people to change conflict into

cooperation is a __ __ __ __ __ __ __ __ __ __.

Vocabulary List

1. destruction
2. division
3. complain
4. debate
5. disturb
6. resist
7. oppose
8. unpleasant
9. object
10. neutral

3 Build New Vocabulary

Base Word Families

For each base word family below, write the base word and a short definition of the base word. Use a dictionary to check your definitions.

1. destruction, destructive, destructible

   _____

2. divided, division, divisible

   _____

3. complains, complainer, complaint

   _____

4. debated, debater, debatable

   _____

5. disturbed, disturbs, disturbance

   _____

6. resisting, resistance, resistant

   _____

7. opposition, opposed, opposes

   _____

8. unpleasant, pleasing, pleasantly

   _____

9. objection, objected, objector

   _____

10. neutrally, neutralize, neutralizer

    _____

Score _____ (Top Score 10)

 **Word Play**

Crossword Puzzle

 Complete the crossword puzzle using the vocabulary words.

ACROSS

2. to say no to

6. the act of breaking or wrecking

8. not taking sides

9. splitting up

10. not nice, unkind

DOWN

1. to be against

3. to talk about faults

4. bother

5. discuss, argue

7. to stand firm against

1. willingly
(wil´ ing lē) *adv.*
in a cheerful and
ready way

2. nowhere
(nō´ hwâr) *adv.*
not in any place

3. fortunately
(fôr´ chə nit lē) *adv.*
luckily; happily

4. faithfully
(fāth´ fəl ē) *adv.*
loyally and
devotedly

5. commonly
(kom´ ən lē) *adv.*
usually; not rare

6. promptly
(prompt´ lē) *adv.*
on time or quickly

7. deliberately
(de lib´ ər it lē) *adv.*
carefully planned

8. precisely
(pri sīs´ lē) *adv.*
perfectly or exactly

9. wearily
(wēr´ ə lē) *adv.*
in a tired way

10. unusually
(un ū´ zhoo lē) *adv.*
not usually, rarely

Adverbs

1 Word Meanings

Using Adverbs

 Read each sentence below. Write the vocabulary word that completes the sentence in the blank.

1. Many species of frogs and snakes

   _____ live near ponds and lakes.

2. When a fly lands on a frog's tongue, the frog

   _____ pulls the fly into its mouth.

3. _____, most poisonous snakes live in areas away from people.

4. After a boa constrictor has trapped its prey, the

   frightened animal has _____ to hide.

5. Boa constrictors deliberately squeeze their prey until

   the animal _____ gives up and stops struggling.

6. No two species of snakes are _____ the same—each is slightly different.

7. Although many people willingly keep snakes as pets,

   these animals never _____ protect their masters or follow them around, as dogs do.

8. If a boa constrictor is strangely and

   _____ still for a few days, this probably means it ate a large meal.

 **Reference Skills**

Using a Thesaurus

 For each word below, write the two words from the word box that have the same or nearly the same meaning. Use a thesaurus to check your answers.

carefully	favorably	quickly	uncommonly
cheerfully	luckily	rapidly	usually
eagerly	often	rarely	watchfully
exactly	perfectly	tiredly	weakly

1. unusually _uncommonly, rarely_

2. precisely _perfectly, exactly_

3. commonly _usually, often_

4. willingly _cheerfully, favorably_ → helpful

5. fortunately _luckily, eagerly_ ↓ long term

6. promptly _quickly, rapidly_

7. wearily _tiredly, weakly_

8. deliberately _watchfully, carefully_

 Think About It

Which vocabulary words are antonyms for the following words: *unluckily, unusual, lively, accidentally, reluctantly.*

Vocabulary List

1. willingly
2. nowhere
3. fortunately
4. faithfully
5. commonly
6. promptly
7. deliberately
8. precisely
9. wearily
10. unusually

3 Build New Vocabulary

Making Adjectives

For each adverb below, write the adjective form and its definition.

1. fortunately _____

2. precisely _____

3. faithfully _____

4. unusually _____

5. promptly _____

6. deliberately _____

• •

The sentences below describe a mystery animal. Circle one of the words in parenthesis that correctly completes each sentence. Then unscramble the words at the bottom of the page to discover what animal is being described.

7. It is *(unusually/unusual)* to see this animal drink because it gets all the water it needs from its food.

8. This animal sleeps about 22 hours per day in a tree and *(fortunate/fortunately)*, is able to hang on to the tree even when it is asleep.

9. It is *(common/commonly)* to find this animal asleep during the day because it eats at night.

10. This animal lives naturally nowhere else in the world except *(precise/precisely)* in Australia.

What kind of animal is being described above?

aolka arbe _____

4 Word Play

Answering Questions

 Read each question below. Write *Yes* or *No* in the blank to answer each question.

1. If you *promptly* do your science project, will it be

   late? _____

2. If you plan your science project *deliberately*, would you expect to get a good grade on it?

   _____

3. If you *willingly* help a friend with her project, do you

   want to help her? _____

4. If you tell your friend *precisely* how to plan her project, should she be able to understand how to

   do it? _____

5. If you *faithfully* help your friend every day with her project, do you sometimes tell her that you won't be

   able to help her? _____

6. If you *commonly* get good grades on your projects,

   do you usually fail them? _____

7. If you *wearily* go up to your room after working on your project, are you ready to go out and play?

   _____

8. If your project turns out to be *unusually* interesting,

   is it boring? _____

Vocabulary Review

1 Review Word Meanings

Read the passage below. Then answer the questions about the boldfaced vocabulary words.

True Friendship Between a Pig and a Spider

In the book *Charlotte's Web,* by E.B. White, Wilbur the pig is lonely and **miserable** until he meets a **clever** spider named Charlotte. Wilbur is very **keen** about Charlotte, and Charlotte soon becomes Wilbur's most **loyal companion.** Wilber **confides** all his secret thoughts to Charlotte, and he **faithfully** follows her advice because he has great **regard** for her **upright** ideas.

Charlotte's **devotion** to Wilbur grows as she sees how **sensitive** he is. She even saves his life by weaving words such as **humble** into her web. When Charlotte's **noble** actions save Wilbur's life, he realizes how **precious** friendship is.

Now read the following questions. Then completely fill in the bubble of the correct answer.

1. Which of the following is an example of *devotion?*
   Ⓐ Charlotte meeting Wilbur
   Ⓑ Wilbur sitting alone
   Ⓒ Charlotte saving Wilbur's life

2. Which of the following is a definition of the word *miserable?*
   Ⓐ very sad
   Ⓑ very loud
   Ⓒ very angry

3. Which of the following means the opposite of *clever?*
   Ⓐ wise
   Ⓑ unwise
   Ⓒ noble

4. In which of the following sentences is the word *humble* correctly defined?
   Ⓐ A person who isn't proud
   Ⓑ A person who is very proud
   Ⓒ A person who is unpleasant

5. Which of the following is an example of something *precious?*
   Ⓐ Charlotte's web
   Ⓑ Wilbur's breakfast
   Ⓒ Charlotte and Wilbur's friendship

6. Which of the following is a synonym of *loyal?*
   Ⓐ funny
   Ⓑ faithful
   Ⓒ interested

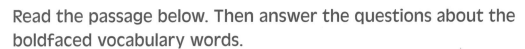

Review Word Meanings

Read the passage below. Then answer the questions about the boldfaced vocabulary words.

When Friends Cooperate

Wilbur and Charlotte were able to become such good friends because they **willingly** worked hard to get along with each other. The **interactions** between them showed how much they cared for each other. Although Charlotte was very **frank** and said **precisely** what was on her mind, she was also very **thoughtful** of Wilbur.

The two friends did not **ignore** problems. Instead, they would have a **debate** about how to **settle** a problem that came up. Charlotte and Wilbur had **mutual** respect for one another and knew how to **cooperate** with one another.

Now read the following questions. Then completely fill in the bubble of the correct answer.

1. Which of the following guide words would be on the same dictionary page as *willingly?*
   Ⓐ wigwam/wilt
   Ⓑ white/wig
   Ⓒ wilt/window

2. Which of the following words best describes Charlotte?
   Ⓐ settle
   Ⓑ debate
   Ⓒ thoughtful

3. Which of the following is a definition of the word *frank?*
   Ⓐ unpleasant
   Ⓑ without pride
   Ⓒ honest and outspoken

4. Which of the following pairs of words are synonyms of the word *precisely?*
   Ⓐ exactly, perfectly
   Ⓑ carefully, mutual
   Ⓒ nearly, almost

5. Which of the following sets of words would you need to alphabetize to the third letter?
   Ⓐ this, thoughtful, thread
   Ⓑ those, thoughtful, thousand
   Ⓒ teach, thoughtful, tickle

6. Which of the following sentences demonstrates the meaning of *debate?*
   Ⓐ Charlotte and Wilbur did not speak during their debates.
   Ⓑ Charlotte and Wilbur had debates because they always agreed.
   Ⓒ Charlotte and Wilbur had debates to settle their problems.

3 Review Word Meanings

Read the passage below. Then answer the questions about the boldfaced vocabulary words.

Conflict in Friendship

When friends **associate** with one another for a long time, sooner or later they have conflicts. One friend's action might be **unpleasant** and might **disturb** the other. Then the second friend might **object** to the first friend's action and **complain** about it to someone else. When friends **resist** trying to settle a conflict, this can cause a **division** in their friendship.

Fortunately, there are many things that friends can do to bring harmony back into their interactions. Friends who have a conflict can avoid the total **destruction** of their friendship if they are **reasonable** and try to settle the conflict. Instead of arguing for a long time and then **wearily** deciding not to speak anymore, friends should **promptly** forgive one another.

hòa

tác động lẫn nhau

sự xung đột

....

Now read the following questions. Then completely fill in the bubble of the correct answer.

1. Which of the following words means "the quality of being unpleasant"?
   Ⓐ promptness
   Ⓑ unpleasantness
   Ⓒ weariness

2. Which of the following words means "in a way that is bothersome"?
   Ⓐ promptly
   Ⓑ disturbingly
   Ⓒ complainingly

3. What is the base word of *fortunately?*
   Ⓐ fortune
   Ⓑ fortunate
   Ⓒ fortunately

4. Based on the passage above, which of the following is true?
   Ⓐ Division helps friendship.
   Ⓑ Friendship is not reasonable.
   Ⓒ Friends should not resist settling conflicts.

5. Which of the following words means "on time or quickly"?
   Ⓐ promptly
   Ⓑ fortunately
   Ⓒ regard

6. Which of the following is a synonym of the word *regard?*
   Ⓐ respect
   Ⓑ reasonable
   Ⓒ resist

 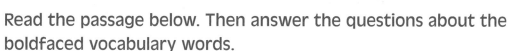

Review Word Meanings

Read the passage below. Then answer the questions about the boldfaced vocabulary words.

Making and Keeping Friends

Most people **commonly** agree that true friendship is one of the most precious things in life. Friendships can begin in **amusing** ways. For example, Lupe and Emma met by bumping into one another on an **unusually** icy sledding hill. Even an unpleasant relationship that seems to be going **nowhere** can lead to a lifelong friendship. John and Lee always **opposed** one another until, one day, they laughed together at a joke. It's good to be **open-minded** about where to make a new friend.

It doesn't take a **genius** to know that keeping a friend means **deliberately** making time and being thoughtful of the other person's needs. Each person must **consent** to being a **reliable** companion if the friendship is to last. Friendships are not **neutral,** because true friends stick up for each other. Just as **harmony** in music is pleasant to the ears, agreement in friendship is pleasant to the heart. Wise friends act on the **suggestion** to forgive more and **judge** less.

Now read the following questions. Then completely fill in the bubble of the correct answer.

1. Does *commonly* mean the opposite of *unusually?*
   - Ⓐ yes
   - Ⓑ no

2. Do you *oppose* something that you feel *neutral* about?
   - Ⓐ yes
   - Ⓑ no

3. Is a *genius* a very *clever* person?
   - Ⓐ yes
   - Ⓑ no

4. If you do something on purpose, do you do it *deliberately?*
   - Ⓐ yes
   - Ⓑ no

5. Does *consent* mean the same as *object?*
   - Ⓐ yes
   - Ⓑ no

6. Is a *reliable* person someone who is always late?
   - Ⓐ yes
   - Ⓑ no

7. Can a *neutral* person help to *settle* a *debate* between two other friends?
   - Ⓐ yes
   - Ⓑ no

8. Does *division* mean the opposite of *harmony?*
   - Ⓐ yes
   - Ⓑ no

1. **permit**
(pûr´ mit) *n.*
order allowing an
action

2. **release**
(ri lēs´) *v.*
to set free

3. **commission**
(kə mish´ ən) *n.*
group gathered for
special duties

4. **reptiles**
(rep´ tilz) *n.*
egg-laying animals
with dry, scaly skin

5. **capture**
(kap´ chər) *v.*
to take by force

6. **mammals**
(mam´ əlz) *n.*
animals that give
birth to live young

7. **pollute**
(pə lōōt´) *v.*
to make dirty

8. **amphibians**
(am fib´ ē ənz) *n.*
egg-laying animals
that live near water

9. **preserve**
(pre zûrv´) *v.*
to make
something last

10. **rescue**
(res´ kū) *v.*
to save from danger

City Wildlife

1 Word Meanings

Sentence Completion

 Write the vocabulary word that correctly
completes each sentence below.

1. We need to clean up the water in the lake rather than
   ___pollute___ it.

2. City planners should _____ city
   parks rather than get rid of them to make room for
   more buildings.

3. Dogs must be kept on a leash in town, but their
   owners can _____ them at the
   park's dog run.

4. A dog owner must have a _____ to
   show that the dog is healthy.

5. It is cruel to _____ a wild animal
   and keep it in a cage.

6. Snakes, lizards, and turtles are _____.

7. Many _____, such as frogs and
   salamanders, live near ponds and rivers and lay their
   eggs in the water.

8. A city often has a _____ that
   decides where to build new parks.

9. Small _____, such as squirrels and
   rabbits, often live in parks.

10. Mother birds sometimes have to
    _____ their chicks when they get
    too close to the edge of the nest.

② Reference Skills
Dictionary Definitions

 Write each vocabulary word next to its dictionary definition below.

1. to save from danger _____

2. a written order allowing an action

   _____

3. warm-blooded animals, such as humans and dogs,

   that bear live babies _____

4. a group that has special duties

   _____

5. to keep something or make it last

   _____

6. to set free or let go _____

7. cold-blooded, egg-laying animals, such as frogs and

   toads, that live near water _____

8. cold-blooded, egg-laying animals, such as snakes and

   lizards, that have dry, scaly skin

   _____

9. to make dirty _____

10. to take by force _____

Vocabulary List

1. permit
2. release
3. commission
4. reptiles
5. capture
6. mammals
7. pollute
8. amphibians
9. preserve
10. rescue

 3 **Build New Vocabulary**

Endings -ed and -ing

 For each verb below, add -ed and -ing to form the verb that shows the action in the past and the action in the present.

Verb	Past	Present
1. release	_____	_____
2. pollute	_____	_____
3. preserve	_____	_____
4. rescue	_____	_____

 Fill in the blanks in the passage below by writing the correct form of a verb from above.

California Sea Lions

California sea lions are large mammals that are sometimes caught and trained for water shows. They live in the Pacific Ocean near the coasts of Canada, the United States, and Mexico. Sea lions are harmed wherever

people are ___*polluted*___ the ocean with plastic trash, waste products, and oil. After past oil spills,

seals and sea lions had to be _____, and the oil was washed off

before they were _____ into a safe area. A government commission has made laws that are

_____ the coasts for sea lions and other ocean wildlife.

Score _____ (Top Score 12) City Wildlife • Build New Vocabulary

4 **Word Play**

Synonyms and Antonyms

 Read each pair of words below and decide whether the words have the same meanings (synonyms) or opposite meanings (antonyms). Circle *S* if the words are synonyms and circle *A* if the words are antonyms.

1. clean   pollute (v)   S   (A)
2. preserve   keep   (S)   A
3. order   permit   (S)   A
4. commission   group   (S)   A
5. save   rescue   (S)   A
6. release   capture   S   (A)
7. pollute   dirty   S   (A)

• •

Write *Yes* or *No* to answer the following questions.

8. If you have a permit to fish at the park, are you allowed to fish? ___Yes___

9. If you preserve a park, are you polluting it?
   ___No___

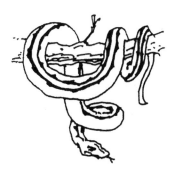

10. Can a mammal be an amphibian? ___yes___

11. Could you rescue a mammal? ___yes___

12. If you capture an animal, are you releasing it?
    ___yes___

Vocabulary List

1. **conservation**
   (kon sər vā´ shən) *n.*
   protection of nature

2. **ozone**
   (ō´ zōn) *n.*
   oxygen gas

3. **algae**
   (al´ jē) *n.*
   simple water plants

4. **recycle**
   (rē sī´ kəl) *v.*
   make ready to use
   again

5. **tropical**
   (trop´ i kəl) *adj.*
   near Earth's equator

6. **survival**
   (sər vī´ vəl) *n.*
   the act of living

7. **fertile**
   (fûr´ təl) *adj.*
   growing and
   producing young

8. **arctic**
   (ärk´ tik) *adj.*
   near the north pole

9. **threatened**
   (thret´ ənd) *adj.*
   likely to die off

10. **waste**
    (wāst) *n.*
    unwanted material

"Environment" Vocabulary

1 Word Meanings

Sentence Completion

Write the vocabulary word that correctly
completes each sentence below.

1. Some _____, such as seaweed
   kelp, can grow to be over 200 feet long.

2. Some _____ seaweed produces
   young by breaking off pieces of itself which take root
   and grow.

3. Algae are important to the _____
   of water animals because they give off oxygen that
   the animals need to live.

4. The lives of many fish and coral reefs have become

   _____ by pollution.

5. It is important to protect the oceans by not allowing

   people to throw _____ in them.

6. People protect Earth's resources when they

   _____ materials so they can
   be reused.

7. The _____ of coral reefs also
   protects many other sea creatures.

8. Very few people live in _____
   areas of the world because it is so cold.

9. _____ areas on Earth are very hot.

10. _____ is a gas found near Earth
    and also high up in the sky.

② Reference Skills

Using an Encyclopedia

 Write each vocabulary word beside the encyclopedia volume in which it can be found.

Volume Number	Guide Words	
1.	1	A/American Elk
2.	2	American Flag/ Arizona
3.	7	Colorado/ Daly City
4.	20	Orthodox/Pier
5.	22	Quarter/Russell
6.	26	Transportation/ Vermeer
7.	27	Vermont/World

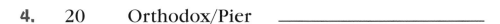

 Sometimes you must look up a related idea to find information about a word in an encyclopedia. Circle the idea that would *most likely* show information related to each vocabulary word below.

8. fertile → *seeds* or *fossils?*

9. survival → *pollution* or *dance?*

10. threatened → *algae* or *endangered?*

Vocabulary List

1. conservation
2. ozone
3. algae
4. recycle
5. tropical
6. survival
7. fertile
8. arctic
9. threatened
10. waste

3 Build New Vocabulary

The Prefix *re-*

 Read each definition below. Write the word that matches each definition by adding the prefix *re-* to one of the base words from the box.

play	write	do	use
make	cycle	gain	heat
build	view	word	move

1. to write again _____

2. to play again _____

3. to do over _____

4. to use again _____

5. to build again _____

6. to get back or have again _____

7. to heat again _____

8. to change the words _____

9. to look at or study again _____

10. to make over _____

11. to get ready for reuse _____

12. to take or move away _____

Score _____ (Top Score 12) "Environment" Vocabulary • Build New Vocabulary

Word Play

What Do You Know?

 Circle *a*, *b*, or *c* to choose the correct answer for each question below.

1. Which is an example of *survival?*
   a. a bean plant being pulled out of the ground
   b. a bean plant growing taller
   c. a bean plant shriveling and dying

2. Which of these is a *threatened* animal and why is it *threatened?*
   a. a Bengal tiger—because people are destroying its forests
   b. a Dalmation dog—because everyone does not want them as pets
   c. a Horse—because people love riding horses

3. Which is an example of *waste?*
   a. a lunchbox full of food waiting to be eaten
   b. a lunchbox full of food being eaten
   c. a lunchbox full of food being thrown away

4. Which animal lives in the *arctic* regions of the world?
   a. a polar bear
   b. a crocodile
   c. a monkey

5. Which kind of weather would be in a *tropical* region of the world?
   a. wind and snow
   b. dry and pleasant
   c. rainy and hot

6. Which is an example of *conservation?*
   a. a girl sitting under a tree
   b. a girl watering a tree
   c. a girl chopping down a tree

1. **collective**
   (kə lek′ tiv) *adj.*
   relating to a group

2. **assemble**
   (ə sem′ bəl) *v.*
   to gather together

3. **network**
   (net′ wûrk) *n.*
   system with
   connected parts

4. **assist**
   (ə sist′) *v.*
   to help

5. **contribution**
   (kon trə bū′ shən) *n.*
   something given

6. **involvement**
   (in volv′ mənt) *n.*
   the act of joining in

7. **resident**
   (rez′ i dənt) *n.*
   one who lives in a
   certain place

8. **traditions**
   (trə dish′ ənz) *n.*
   beliefs handed down

9. **customary**
   (kus′ tə mâr′ ē) *adj.*
   usual   *thường, thói quen, theo lệ thường*

10. **immigrant**
    (im′ i grənt) *n.*
    person living in a
    new country

Vocabulary for Communities

1 Word Meanings

Categorization *hệ thống*

phân loại

Classify the vocabulary words by writing each
one under the correct category below. Each
vocabulary word is only used once.

1. Old Habits

   traditions

   customary

2. Groups

   collective

   involvement

3. Helping

   assist   contribution

4. People

   resident   immigrant

5. Interacting   *tác dụng làm nhau*

   assemble   collective

• •

Think About It

If a *network* is a system with connected parts, could a
network be a spider web? Could a *network* be the water
pipes in a building? What other kinds of *networks* can you
think of?

② Reference Skills

Alphabetical Order

 Write the words in each group of words below in alphabetical order.

1. tropical, traditions, trial

traditions, trial, tropical.

2. involvement, interaction, instant

instant, interaction, involvement

3. aside, assist, asleep

aside, asleep, assist

4. immigrant, imagine, important

imagine, immigrand, important,

5. ashore, assemble, asking

ashore, asking, assemble

6. contribution, companion, cooperation

companion, cooperation, contribution,

7. curious, customary, cupboard

cupboard, curious, customary

8. neutral, nervous, network

nervous, network, neutral

9. consumer, commission, collective

collective, commission, consumer

10. resident, release, recycle

recycle, release, resident.

Vocabulary List

1. collective
2. assemble
3. network
4. assist
5. contribution
6. involvement *than giữ*
7. resident
8. traditions
9. customary
10. immigrant

He is involved in the plot : nó' co' dự, nhúng tay vào 1 âm mưu

3 Build New Vocabulary

Base Word Families

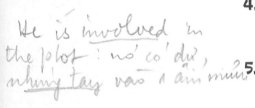
Write the base word for each base word family below.

1. assembly, assemblage, (assembled)

    _____ assemble _____

2. (involved), involvement, (involving)

    _____ involve _____

3. (collective,) collector, collection

    _____ collect _____

• •

Circle the word that correctly completes each sentence.

4. A *(networking /* (network)*)* is a system with connected parts.

5. To *(*(immigrate) */ immigrant)* means to move to another country.

6. An *(immigrate /* (immigrant)*)* is a person who has moved to a new country.

7. A person who lives in a certain place is called a *(reside /* (resident)*)*.

8. To *(*(reside) */ resident)* in a place means to live there.

9. A *(*(tradition) */ traditional)* is a belief or way of doing something that is handed down in families.

10. *(Tradition /* (Traditional)*)* holidays are those that people have celebrated for a long time.

 ## 4 Word Play

Mystery Words

 dấu mới = dew

 Use the word meaning <u>clues</u> and underlined words in each <u>riddle</u> below to help you figure out the vocabulary word. Write each vocabulary word in the boxes.

 bí ẩn, câu đố

1. Oh <u>Mary</u>, you are always following the usual <u>customs</u>.

| c | u | (s) | t | o | m | a | r | y |

2. <u>Grant</u> just moved to the country of <u>Immi</u>.

| I | (m) | m | i | g | r | a | n | t |

3. Miss <u>Ibution</u> is always <u>contribu</u>ting and giving things away.

| C | O | N | T | R | (I) | B | U | T | I | O | N |

4. "It is <u>as</u> hard to gather things," said Dr. <u>Semble</u>, "as it is to put them in order."

| a | s | s | e | m | b | (L) | e |

5. A spider spins a <u>working</u> <u>net</u> by connecting threads so it can catch flies.

| n | (e) | t | w | o | r | k |

 Write the circled letters from above in the blank below to make a word that completes this sentence:

6. A _____smile_____ is something you can share with anyone, even if the person doesn't speak your language.

Vocabulary for Government

① Word Meanings

Sentence Completion

1. cabinet
   (kab´ ə nit) n.
   group that advises
   a leader

2. candidate
   (kan´ di dāt) n.
   person trying to
   get elected

3. control   ra lệnh
   (kən trōl´) n.
   power over others

4. repeal   huỷ bỏ²
   (ri pēl´) v.   làm lại
   to officially take
   back

5. military
   (mil´ i târ´ ē) n.
   armed forces

6. negotiate   điều đình
   (ni gō´ shē āt) v.   thương thuyết
   to try to reach
   agreement

7. term
   (tûrm) n.
   period of time

8. legislate
   (lej´ is lāt) v.
   to make laws

9. petition
   (pə tish´ ən) n.
   written request

10. tax
    (taks´) n.
    money paid
    to government

Complete each sentence below by writing the correct vocabulary word in the blank.

1. People in the United States have to pay
   _____ tax _____ on the money they make
   from working.

2. A citizen who wants a law changed or repealed can
   sign a _____ petition _____.

3. The _____ term _____ of office for the
   president of the United States is four years.

4. The main people who give advice to the president are
   the members of his or her _____ cabinet _____.

5. The president has control of the armed forces, which
   means he or she is in charge of the U. S.
   _____ military _____.   ?

6. Senators and members of the House of Representatives
   often have to _____ negotiate _____ for a long time
   before they agree.

7. When senators and members of the House of
   Representatives _____ repeal _____, they make
   laws for the whole country.

8. A person who is trying to be elected president of the
   United States controls who the
   _____ candidate _____ for vice-president will be.

② Reference Skills

Using a Glossary *bảng kê ~ chữ khó.*

candidate	group that	(kan´ di dāt)
(kab´ ə nit)	advises a leader	cabinet
power over others	(kən trōl´) control	person trying to get elected

Alphabetize the vocabulary words from the box above on the lines below. Then write their phonetic spellings and definitions beside them to create a glossary entry.

1. _____

   _____

2. _____

   _____

3. _____

   _____

• •

Circle *Yes* or *No* to answer the following questions about using a glossary.
bảng kê ~ chữ khó.

4. Will a glossary help you to understand how a word is used in the book? (Yes) No

5. Can a glossary help you when you do not have a dictionary? (Yes) No

6. Are glossaries usually found at the front of books? Yes (No)

Vocabulary List

1. cabinet

2. candidate

3. control

4. repeal huỷ bỏ

5. military

6. negotiate đàm phán thương thuyết

7. term

8. legislate v làm luật

9. petition yêu cầu

10. tax

3 Build New Vocabulary

Endings -s and -es

Read each definition below. Decide whether the word should be singular or plural. Choose the word it is describing from the box and write it on the line.

Petition–Petitions	Term–Terms	Boss–Bosses
Military–Militaries	Branch–Branches	Tax–Taxes
Witness–Witnesses	Candidate–Candidates	
Leader–Leaders	Judge–Judges	

1. many requests to a leader _petitions_

2. several periods of time _term_

3. person in charge of workers

   boss

4. armed forces _military_

5. part or division of a whole _branches_

6. all the money paid to the government

   taxes

7. person who saw an action _witness_ (không thấy mới)

8. person trying to get elected _candidate_

9. people who are in charge _leaders_

10. person in charge in a court of law

    judge

 **4** **Word Play**

Answering Questions

 Circle *Yes* or *No* to answer each question below.

1. Can a person give a petition to government leaders?
(Yes) No

2. Can a candidate repeal a law? Yes (No)

3. Could a term negotiate with the president? Yes (No)

4. Do citizens of the United States pay taxes? (Yes) No

5. Can the members of a cabinet negotiate a problem?
(Yes) No

6. Does the military control the President of the United
States? Yes (No)

7. Could a person repeal something she said? (Yes) No

8. Could a cabinet become the President of the United
States? Yes (No)

9. Can a petition pay tax to the government? (Yes) No

10. Could a cabinet legislate a candidate? (Yes) No

 ## Think About It

If you could give a petition to the government of the
United States, what would it say? Would you ask for a
law to be repealed or for a new law to be legislated?

Vocabulary List

1. **pause**
   (pôz) v.
   to stop for a short
   while

2. **rifle**
   (rī′ fəl) v.
   to search through
   and rob

3. **acquire**
   (ə kwīr′) v.
   to gain or get

4. **emerge**
   (i mûrj′) v.
   to come out

5. **grasp**
   (grasp) v.
   to firmly hold

6. **absorb**
   (ab sorb′) v.
   to soak up

7. **indicate**
   (in′ di kāt) v.
   to show or point out

8. **log**
   (lôg) v.
   to write in
   a record book

9. **seize**
   (sēz) v.
   to take suddenly

10. **flee**
    (flē) v.
    to run away from
    danger

Action Words

1 **Word Meanings**

Synonyms

 Write each vocabulary word next to the word below that has the same or nearly the same meaning.

1. stop _____pause_____

2. clutch _____

3. snatch _____

4. appear _____

5. get _____acquire_____

6. show _____indicate_____

7. steal _____

8. write _____log_____

9. soak _____absorb_____

10. run _____flee_____

● ●

🔆 Think About It

If a robber was *rifling* something, what two other vocabulary words could describe how the robber would hold the stolen objects?

② Reference Skills

Multiple Meanings

 Read the dictionary definitions below. Complete each sentence with the correct word.

---

grasp (grasp) *v.* **1.** to take hold of firmly: *The baseball player grasped the bat.* **2.** to understand: *Some school subjects are hard for students to grasp.*

log (log) *v.* **1.** to cut down trees: *The workers are ready to log the forest.* **2.** to record in a logbook: *The captain logged the progress of the ship.*

tax (taks) *n.* **1.** money that must be paid by people to support the government: *People must pay tax on the money they earn.* **2.** a heavy burden or strain: *The extra homework put a tax on my brain.*

---

1. The long climb up the mountain path put a

   _____ on our strength.

2. Many students find math easy to

   _____ .

3. The campers plan to _____ the
   number of miles they hiked every day.

4. The ice-skaters often _____ one
   another's hands while they perform tricks.

5. Many people believe that companies should not be

   allowed to _____ the rain forests.

Vocabulary List

1. *pause*

2. *rifle*

3. *acquire*

4. *emerge*

5. *grasp* nắm lấy, ôm lấy.

6. *absorb*

7. *indicate*

8. *log* khuyết, ghi chép vật gì vào sổ phát cur

9. *seize*

10. *flee*

3 Build New Vocabulary

Context Clues

 Circle the form of the vocabulary word that correctly completes each sentence below.

1. A rabbit will quickly *(flee / grasp)* if it sees a car coming toward it.

2. I was amazed by the amount of water that the natural sponge *(absorbed / acquired)*.

3. After *(indicating / emerging)* from her den, the mother wolf looked around to be sure there was no danger to her cubs.

4. The wind began to blow and clouds gathered, *(pausing / indicating)* that a rainstorm was coming.

5. Olympic soccer champion Mia Hamm *(acquired / fled)* her will to win by playing soccer when she was a child.

6. The police caught the thief *(emerging / rifling)* through our house.

7. Fortunately, they *(seized / absorbed)* the thief before he could escape.

8. Unfortunately for him, he *(paused / fled)* just long enough for the officers to grasp him.

9. A nurse must know about caring for patients as well as *(indicating / logging)* information about their progress.

10. The underwater diver *(grasped / aquired)* the side of the boat and pulled herself aboard.

Word Play

Homograph Puns

 Complete each pun below with words from the word box. *lời nói cột, chư đồng âm dị nghĩa*

> *grasp:* **1.** to grab firmly; **2.** understanding of something
> *frank:* **1.** outspoken and honest; **2.** a hot dog
> *cabinet:* **1.** group that advises a leader; **2.** a cupboard for storing things
> *taxed:* **1.** tired because of difficult demands; **2.** to be made to pay money to the government
> *log:* **1.** a record book; **2.** a piece of wood
> *sharp:* **1.** smart; **2.** having an edge that cuts

1. Why didn't the president get any advice? Because he had the ___cabinet___ shut up.

2. What did the pen say to the smart scissors? "You're ___sharp___ as a tack!"

3. What do you call an honest and outspoken hot dog? A _____ _____.

4. Why did the student put his record book in the fireplace? Because it was a ___log (nhật ký)___.

5. What do you say when you understand a hold in wrestling? I _____ the _____.

chiến đấu (vickhỏ khăn vật lộn (wrestlif

6. Why did the woman go straight to bed after giving money to the government? She had been ___taxed___.

Vocabulary Review

Review Word Meanings

Read the passage below. Then answer the questions about the boldfaced vocabulary words.

City Wildlife

Mammals, birds, **reptiles,** fish, **amphibians,** insects, and plants make up the many different kinds of wildlife that are welcome sights in cities. However, sometimes governments must make laws to protect the environment and take **control** over some forms of wildlife. For example, **algae** can become too **fertile** and reproduce so fast that they **absorb** all the oxygen and threaten other life forms in park ponds. Mosquitoes and rats can carry diseases, and birds can **pollute** park fountains. It takes a lot of work to maintain wildlife environments in the city.

Now read the following questions. Then completely fill in the bubble of the correct answer.

1. What words in the passage above mean the same as *fertile?*
   Ⓐ "reproduce so fast"
   Ⓑ "use up all the oxygen"
   Ⓒ "threaten other life forms"

2. Which of the following is a definition of *algae?*
   Ⓐ simple water plants
   Ⓑ tiny water bugs
   Ⓒ dead leaves

3. Which of the following means the opposite of *pollute?*
   Ⓐ to make dirty
   Ⓑ to clean up
   Ⓒ to litter

4. To which group do horses, dogs, and mice belong?
   Ⓐ mammals
   Ⓑ reptiles
   Ⓒ amphibians

5. Which of the following words has the meanings "power to others" and "to hold within limits; restrain"?
   Ⓐ control
   Ⓑ seize
   Ⓒ absorb

6. Which of the following is *not* an example of an amphibian?
   Ⓐ frog
   Ⓑ salamander
   Ⓒ fish

② Review Word Meanings

Read the passage below. Then answer the questions about the boldfaced vocabulary words.

Wildlife Visitors

Some forms of wildlife are city **residents,** while others are just visiting. In some places, people have a **tradition** of watching flocks of birds fly south to their winter homes. Other animals that **emerge** from their homes in nature and wander into cities must be **captured** to prevent them from hurting people. In **arctic** climates, polar bears can become dangerous visitors. Fortunately, they can be caught and then **released** into a wilderness area. It takes a **network** of people and organizations to safely relocate and **preserve** these wildlife guests.

Now read the following questions. Then completely fill in the bubble of the correct answer.

1. Which of the following means the opposite of *arctic?*
   - Ⓐ cold
   - Ⓑ tropical
   - Ⓒ north

2. Which of the following is a verb that means "to take care of"?
   - Ⓐ emerge
   - Ⓑ preserve
   - Ⓒ tradition

3. Which of the following is a definition of *resident* in the passage above?
   - Ⓐ an animal who just arrived in a country
   - Ⓑ an animal who moves away from a certain place
   - Ⓒ an animal who lives in a certain place

4. In which sentence below is *emerge* used correctly?
   - Ⓐ The foxes will soon emerge from their den.
   - Ⓑ Sometimes people have to emerge wild animals.
   - Ⓒ It takes a lot of work to emerge city parks.

5. Which of the following words from the passage above means "to set free"?
   - Ⓐ preserve
   - Ⓑ network
   - Ⓒ release

 **Review Word Meanings**

Read the passage below. Then answer the questions about the boldfaced vocabulary words.

Ways to Protect the Environment

The government must **legislate** good laws to make sure that **conservation** is working. When a problem related to the environment is found, a **commission** is formed to think of ways to solve the problem. Individual people can help solve environmental problems, too. They can sign a **petition** that suggests a way to solve a problem. They also can help to **negotiate** the best plan for protecting the environment. People working together in a **collective** effort can make a big difference. They also help protect the environment when they **recycle** empty containers and other forms of **waste.**

Now read the following questions. Then completely fill in the bubble of the correct answer.

1. Which of the following words in the passage above means "unwanted material"?
   Ⓐ collective
   Ⓑ negotiate
   Ⓒ waste

2. Which of the following means the same as *recycle?*
   Ⓐ reuse
   Ⓑ use up
   Ⓒ useless

3. Which of the following is a definition of *negotiate?*
   Ⓐ to pass a law
   Ⓑ to try to reach an agreement
   Ⓒ to control

4. In which sentence below is *collective* used correctly?
   Ⓐ The students made a collective decision to go on a field trip.
   Ⓑ The students collective decided to take a bus.
   Ⓒ The students collective money to pay for the field trip.

5. Which of the following words means the opposite of *conservation?*
   Ⓐ protection
   Ⓑ destruction
   Ⓒ preservation

6. What is *negotiated* in the passage above?
   Ⓐ empty containers
   Ⓑ a plan to help the environment
   Ⓒ good laws

4 Review Word Meanings

Read the passage below. Then answer the questions about the boldfaced vocabulary words.

People Making A Difference

People's **involvement** with the environment can take the form of **contributions** of time and money. Many people **assemble** to plan ways to ensure the **survival** of **threatened** animals and to protect **tropical** rain forests. Others try to conserve energy so that there is less pollution, which **assists** in protecting the layer of **ozone** above Earth.

Now read the following questions. Then completely fill in the bubble of the correct answer.

1. Which of the following is a definition of *contributions?*
   Ⓐ things that must be done right away
   Ⓑ things that are taken away
   Ⓒ things that are given

2. Which of the following is a definition of *tropical?*
   Ⓐ very hot and located near the equator
   Ⓑ very dry and located in a desert
   Ⓒ very cold and located near the north pole

3. When an animal is *threatened,* it is _____.
   Ⓐ a very dangerous animal
   Ⓑ likely to die off
   Ⓒ unable to survive in tropical places

4. Which of the following means the same as *assists?*
   Ⓐ helps
   Ⓑ harms
   Ⓒ acquires

5. In which of the following sentences is *involvement* used as it is used in the passage above?
   Ⓐ The students' involvement helped to preserve the park.
   Ⓑ The students' assistance helped to preserve the involvement of the park.
   Ⓒ The involvement was for the students to preserve the park.

6. Which of the following is true about *ozone?*
   Ⓐ It is a gas above Earth.
   Ⓑ It is a liquid on Earth.
   Ⓒ It is a solid upon Earth.

Vocabulary List

1. **invisible**
(in viz′ ə bəl) *adj.*
not able to be seen

2. **conceal**
(kən sēl′) *v.*
to hide or cover

3. **invent**
(in vent′) *v.*
to create

4. **fantasy**
(fan′ tə sē) *n.*
make-believe;
imagination

5. **magnificent**
(mag nif′ ə sənt) *adj.*
wonderful; beautiful

6. **heroic**
(hi rō′ ik) *adj.*
brave and honorable

7. **mental**
(men′ təl) *adj.*
of the mind

8. **fiction**
(fik′ shən) *n.*
stories that are
made up

9. **transform**
(trans form′) *v.*
to change into
something else

10. **enchant**
(en chant′) *v.*
to delight

"Imagination" Vocabulary

 **1** **Word Meanings**

Synonyms

 Write each vocabulary word next to its pair of synonyms below. Use a dictionary if you need help.

1. please, delight _____

2. change, alter _____

3. stories, tales _____

4. cover, hide _____

5. make-believe, imagination _____

 Write the vocabulary word that is a synonym for the underlined word in each sentence below.

6. Gerda uses her <u>intellectual</u> cleverness to save Kay in the story of "The Snow Queen." _____

7. C. S. Lewis <u>created</u> the country of Narnia in *The Lion, the Witch, and the Wardrobe.* _____

8. The leaping panther was really <u>amazing</u>.

_____

9. In fairy tales a <u>courageous</u> character always helps someone in trouble. _____

10. In *The Hobbit,* Bilbo finds a ring that makes him <u>unseen.</u> _____

2 Reference Skills

Phonetic Spellings and Definitions

Write each vocabulary word next to its phonetic spelling. Use slashes to show where each word is divided into syllables.

1. (trans form´) _____

2. (men´ təl) _____

3. (en chant´) _____

4. (mag nif´ ə sənt) _____

5. (fan´ tə sē) _____

6. (kən sēl´) _____

• •

Write the vocabulary word from above that matches each definition below.

7. to delight _____

8. to cover or keep hidden _____

9. relating to the mind _____

10. to change into something else

_____

11. very beautiful and special _____

12. outside of reality; make-believe _____

• •

 ## Think About It

Try pronouncing the words above with the stress on the wrong syllable. Would you recognize that word if someone said it that way?

Vocabulary List

1. invisible
2. conceal
3. invent
4. fantasy
5. magnificent
6. heroic
7. mental
8. fiction
9. transform
10. enchant

3 Build New Vocabulary

Context Clues

Write the vocabulary word that best completes each sentence below.

1. A _____ is something that is not real.

2. Jack had to _____ the gold because he was afraid his cow might steal it.

3. Paloma could tell such marvelous stories that she would _____ us with them.

4. A story that you make up is _____.

5. In the story of Rumpelstiltskin, a tiny man promised to _____ straw into gold, but he was not doing it to be kind.

6. A _____ action, like ignoring a bully, takes great bravery.

7. The gown for the ball was beautiful and _____, but Cinderella wished it was comfortable like her jogging suit.

8. He realized after he wished to be _____ that if people cannot see you, you get bumped and stepped on a lot.

9. She used her mind and made a _____ calculation of how far she could fly with her new wings.

10. When writing a story you should _____, or create, characters.

 **4** **Word Play**

Alliteration

 Complete each alliterative sentence below with the vocabulary word that best fits.

1. _____ ink is incredibly interesting!

2. Tawana takes tired tomatoes to

   _____ into tasty treats.

3. Elephants, eels, and elks _____ me.

4. The magical moon lit up many

   _____ mountains in Montana.

5. The cats can't continue to _____ their cruel claws.

6. Hanako had high hopes that a

   _____ human would help her.

7. Fernando's favorite _____ was to be a famous fullback in football.

8. Ivan uses his imagination to _____ images.

Think About It

What alliterative sentences could you invent that use the words *mental* and *fiction?* What other vocabulary words could you use in those two sentences?

1. **fierce**
(firs) *adj.*
wild and forceful

2. **unfamiliar**
(un fə mil' yər) *adj.*
strange; unknown

3. **hostile**
(hos' təl) *adj.*
unfriendly; showing
hate

4. **mighty**
(mī' tē) *adj.*
powerful

5. **suitable**
(soo' tə bəl) *adj.*
just right; fitting

6. **shallow**
(shal' ō) *adj.*
not deep

7. **famous**
(fā' məs) *adj.*
known by many

8. **gallant**
(gal' ənt) *adj.*
courageous

9. **adorable**
(ə dor' ə bəl) *adj.*
lovable and
charming

10. **slippery**
(slip' ə rē) *adj.*
causing to slip
or slide

Adjectives

 Word Meanings

Examples

 Write the vocabulary word that describes each example below.

1. The ocean wave came crashing down, pounding the shallow water near the shore. What word describes

   the power of the wave? _____

2. The soaring eagle glided above the plain, wild and forceful. What word describes the eagle?

   _____

3. Almost everyone in the United States knows who the president is. What word describes the president?

   _____

4. Gallant Jamaal slid across the ice, laughing. What

   word describes the ice? _____

5. She had never been in this forest before. What word

   describes the forest? _____

6. The bully fought with everyone. What word

   describes the bully? _____

7. There was a strong wind and a clear sky; it was a perfect day to fly a kite. What word describes

   this idea? _____

8. The tiny puppy curled up in Kachira's lap, making her smile. What word describes the puppy?

   _____

② Reference Skills

Base Words and Definitions

Circle *a*, *b*, or *c* to choose the correct base word for each vocabulary word below.

1. unfamiliar
   a. familiar   **b.** unfamily   **c.** mill

2. suitable
   a. table   **b.** able   **c.** suit

3. famous
   a. mous   **b.** fame   **c.** family

4. adorable (9)
   a. adore   **b.** able   **c.** ad

5. slippery (a) (đất) trơn trượt, o chắc chắn, giao xào.
   a. lip   **b.** slip   **c.** slipper   giày đi trong nhà.

• •

Write each base word from above next to its correct definition below.

6. to be just right ___ suitable ___

7. to lose one's balance or footing
   ___ slippery ___

8. to love ___

9. being well known by many people
   ___ famous ___

10. commonly seen, heard, or experienced
    ___

Vocabulary List

1. *fierce*
2. *unfamiliar*
3. *hostile*
4. *mighty*
5. *suitable*
6. *shallow*
7. *famous*
8. *gallant*
9. *adorable*
10. *slippery*

3 Build New Vocabulary

Adverbs with -ly

 Add the suffix *-ly* to the following adjectives to make adverbs.

1. hostile _____

2. gallant _____

3. fierce _____

4. invisible _____

 Using the adverbs from above, answer the questions below.

5. Which adverb means the opposite of *kindly?*

_____

6. Which adverb means the opposite of *cowardly?*

_____

7. Which adverb means the opposite of *gently?*

_____

8. Which adverb means the opposite of *visibly?*

_____

💡 Think About It

Could someone who paints famously not be a famous person? Could someone play soccer fiercely but not be a fierce person?

Score _____ (Top Score 8) Adjectives • Build New Vocabulary

Word Play

Oxymorons

 Choose the oxymoron from the box below that matches each example. Remember that an oxymoron combines two words that are opposites.

A familiar mystery	A wise fool
A suitable mismatch	A loud silence
A gallant coward	

1. Hu-lan had never seen this strange puzzle before, but at the same time she felt like she had.

   _____

2. Even though the room was silent, everyone was mad. It was like they were yelling by being quiet.

   _____

3. Justin's clothes never match but they still seem just right.

   _____

4. The Cowardly Lion was scared, but he decided to help save Dorothy anyway.

   _____

5. The silly clown always acted like he didn't know anything. However, when his friends needed help, he gave them wise advice.

   _____

Vocabulary List

1. **pioneer**
   (pī ə nir´) *n.*
   first person to explore

2. **conquer**
   (kong´ kər) *v.*
   to take over by force

3. **harsh** *thô, nhám*
   (härsh) *adj.* *bản nhám*
   rough and *quan*
   unpleasant

4. **frontier** *ranh giới*
   (frun tir´) *n.*
   beginning of
   unsettled land

5. **inspect**
   (in spekt´) *v.*
   to look at carefully

6. **supply**
   (sə plī´) *n.*
   a needed thing

7. **fleet**
   (flēt) *n.*
   a group of boats

8. **compass**
   (kum´ pəs) *n.*
   tool that shows
   directions

9. **colony**
   (kol´ ə nē) *n.*
   land ruled by
   another country

10. **prospector**
    (pros´ pek tər) *n.*
    one who explores
    for riches

h đi tìm vàng (mỏ)

"Exploration" Vocabulary

 1 **Word Meanings**

Base Word Families

 Write the vocabulary word that belongs with each base word family below.

1. inspector, inspection, inspected, inspecting
   inspect

2. fleets, fleeting, fleetly, fleetness _____

3. prospect, prospects, prospected, prospecting
   prospect hy vọng, tương lai

4. colonist, colonize, colonization, colonial
   colony

5. frontiers, frontiersman
   frontier

6. conqueror, conquest, conquerable, conquers
   conquer

7. supplies, supplier, suppliers, supplied
   supply

8. compasses, compassable, compasser, encompass
   compass

9. harshly, harshness, harshen, harshened
   harsh

10. pioneers, pioneered, pioneering
    pioneer

2 Reference Skills

Words with Multiple Meanings

 Read the dictionary entries below. Then read each sentence and look at the underlined word. Write the number of the definition of the underlined word as it is used in each sentence.

fleet **1.** *n.* a group of ships or cars **2.** *adj.* swift, fast.

1. In 1862 Alexandrine Tinné took a small <u>fleet</u> to explore the Nile River of Africa. _____

2. Tinné's boats were <u>fleet</u>, and her group arrived at the meeting place ahead of John Speke's group. _____

pioneer **1.** *n.* a first explorer or settler **2.** *v.* to explore or settle in a place

3. On July 20, 1969, Armstrong <u>pioneered</u> the first landing on the moon. _____

4. Astronaut Neil Armstrong was a <u>pioneer</u> of space travel. _____

compass **1.** *n.* an instrument that shows directions, such as north and south **2.** *v.* to go around something

5. Some orbiting telescopes <u>compass</u> Earth as they travel in space. _____

6. A <u>compass</u> would not help you locate directions on the moon because it works with Earth's north pole.

_____

Vocabulary List

1. pioneer
2. conquer
3. harsh
4. frontier
5. inspect
6. supply
7. fleet
8. compass
9. colony
10. prospector

3 Build New Vocabulary

The Suffixes *-er* and *-or*

 Read the sentences below. Complete each sentence by choosing the *-er* or *-or* word from the box. Write the word in the blank.

| explorer | villagers | inspector | supplier |
| prospectors | inventor | miners | conquerors |

1. In 1893 Mary Henrietta Kingsley sailed to Africa and became the first European _____ of Gabon.

2. She studied the customs of the native _____ and African peoples.

3. Mary Kingsley wrote many books about Africa. She was a _____ of information to European people.

4. Antonie van Leeuwenhoek created the first microscope that could see bacteria. He was an _____.

5. As an _____ of tiny things, he carefully looked at skin, hair, and bacteria.

6. Spanish _____ took over Mexico and Peru in the 1500s.

7. Many of them were _____ looking for riches.

8. Silver was one of the treasures that _____ dug from the ground and sent back to Spain.

Score _____ (Top Score 8) "Exploration" Vocabulary • Build New Vocabulary

4 **Word Play**

Exploration Time Line

Complete each time line entry with the correct vocabulary word.

19|00

 1862 Explorer Alexandrine Tinné's

   _____sails on the Nile River.

 1849 Almost every _____ rushes
   to California in search of gold.

 1832 The Oregon Trail becomes the main route for
   the wagon trains of any

   _____

   who intends to settle in the West. The journey

   is _____ and difficult.

 1807 Robert Fulton invents a steamboat that allows

   _____ shipments to travel
   quickly to people who need food.

 1803 Lewis and Clark become the first Americans to

   explore the western _____.

18|00

17|00

 1668 Antonie van Leeuwenhoek invents a
   microscope that allows him to

   _____ bacteria.

 1607 Jamestown becomes the first English

   _____ in America.

16|00

Vocabulary List

1. **create**
(krē āt') *v.*
to make

2. **estimate**
(es' tə māt) *v.*
to make a good
guess

3. **realize**
(rē' ə līz) *v.*
to know

4. **intelligence**
(in tel' i jəns) *n.*
understanding

5. **educate**
(ej' ə kāt) *v.*
to teach

6. **conscious**
(kon' shəs) *adj.*
awake and aware

7. **logical**
(loj' i kəl) *adj.*
making good sense

8. **concentration**
(kon sən trā' shən) *n.*
close attention

9. **decision**
(di sizh' ən) *n.*
a choice made

10. **consider**
(kən sid' ər) *v.*
to carefully think

Vocabulary for Thinking

1 Word Meanings

Sentence Completion

 Write the vocabulary word that best completes each sentence below.

1. A carpenter can _____ how long it will take to build a cabinet.

2. The answer to a math problem should be

_____.

3. People are usually not fully _____ when they first wake up in the morning.

4. Trying to learn a new sport takes a lot of

_____.

5. A judge must think about all the facts before making

a _____ about a case.

6. Most people _____ that it is important to get along with others.

7. Government leaders must carefully

_____ when they make new laws.

8. It is important to use your _____ to do well in school.

9. To _____ a painting or story is like giving your mind a chance to play.

10. Teachers try to _____ their students.

② Reference Skills
Definitions and Base Words

 Write the vocabulary word that matches each definition.

1. to know _____

2. a judgement made or a choice settled on

   _____

3. well-thought out; reasonable _____

4. to teach or train someone _____

5. the ability to learn and understand

   _____

6. awake and aware of what is going on

   _____

7. to make _____

• •

Write the base word of each vocabulary word below. Use a dictionary if you need help.

8. decision _____

9. unconsciousness _____

10. logical _____

11. creativity _____

12. concentration _____

Vocabulary List

1. create
2. estimate
3. realize
4. intelligence
5. educate
6. conscious
7. logical
8. concentration
9. decision
10. consider

3 Build New Vocabulary

The Prefix *un-*

Choose the word from the box to complete each sentence below.

uneducated	unconscious	unsuitable
unexpected	unwilling	uncommonly

1. In 1873 Chester Greenwood decided that wool

   hats were _____ because they
   were so itchy.

2. Chester invented something that is worn on the ears

   in _____ cold weather. He invented
   earmuffs!

3. One evening in 1972, ten-year-old Becky Schroeder
   was writing at night in the family car. She was

   _____ to stop writing just because
   it was dark.

4. She was _____ about things that
   glow in the dark, so she went to the library and
   found out about a special paint.

5. Becky covered a clipboard with glow-in-the-dark
   paint. She was delighted to find that it worked

   _____ well. Now she could write
   in the dark.

6. If Becky had been asleep and

   _____ in the car, she would never
   have invented her special clipboard.

4 **Word Play**

Name Another One

 Choose a word from the box below that is a synonym for each boldfaced vocabulary word. Write the word in the blank to finish each rhyme.

| knows | brains | think | wise | choice | guess |

1. Hesitant Hetty **considers** each blink—she won't ever

   decide, she will only just _____.

2. Hetty's quite **logical,** her brain's quite a prize. Her thoughts are so thoughtful, her thinker's so

   _____.

3. First Hetty **estimates,** I have to confess. But she can't stop at that—no, Hetty won't

   _____.

4. She then will ask others whose **intelligence** she gains. They give her good answers by using their

   _____.

5. But after much thinking, no **decision** to rejoice. She won't stop her thinking, no, she won't make a

   _____.

6. Hetty knows of this trouble—I **realize** she

   _____. But she just likes to think, not decide, I suppose.

1. **glitter**
(glit´ ər) v.
to shine brightly

2. **grubby**
(grub´ ē) adj.
dirty

3. **baggy**
(bag´ ē) adj.
hanging loosely

4. **bony**
(bō´ nē) adj.
very thin

5. **feeble**
(fē´ bəl) adj.
weak

6. **spectacular**
(spek tak´ yə lər)
adj.
wonderful and
amazing

7. **attractive**
(ə trak´ tiv) adj.
good-looking

8. **glossy**
(glô´ sē) adj.
shiny

9. **muscular**
(mus´ kyə lər) adj.
having strong
muscles

10. **crooked**
(kro͝ok´ id) adj.
bent

Vocabulary for Appearances

1 Word Meanings

Sentence Completion

Complete each sentence below with the vocabulary word that makes the most sense.

1. Pigs are _____ because they roll in mud to keep themselves cool.

2. Greyhounds are so tall and thin that they look very

   _____ even when they are very muscular.

3. A dog from China called a shar-pei has extra folds of

   skin that are wrinkled and _____.

4. After a good brushing, a horse's coat looks attractive, silky, and

   _____.

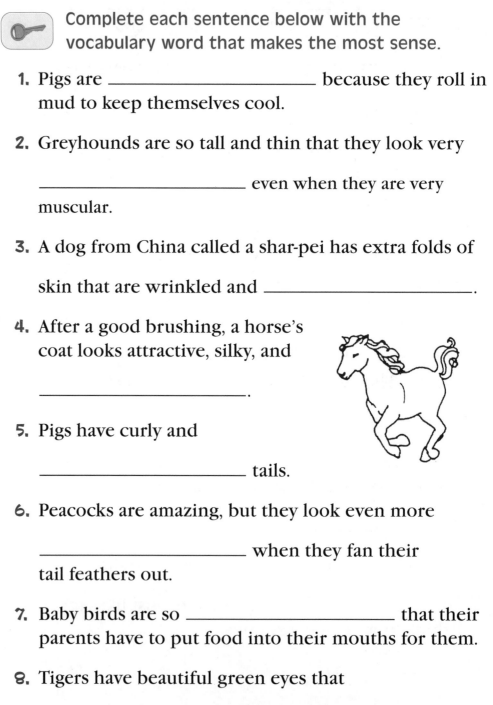

5. Pigs have curly and

   _____ tails.

6. Peacocks are amazing, but they look even more

   _____ when they fan their tail feathers out.

7. Baby birds are so _____ that their parents have to put food into their mouths for them.

8. Tigers have beautiful green eyes that

   _____ in the dark.

2 Reference Skills

Using a Thesaurus

Write the vocabulary word that is a synonym of each pair of words below. Use a thesaurus to help you.

1. sparkle, twinkle _____

2. shiny, sleek _____

3. dirty, dusty _____

4. slack, loose _____

5. skinny, thin _____

6. weak, frail _____

7. wonderful, magnificent _____

8. beautiful, good-looking _____

9. strong, powerful _____

10. bent, twisted _____

• •

 Think About It

What would a *bony* and *feeble* animal look like? How about a *muscular* and *attractive* animal? What two vocabulary words could describe an old bookbag?

Vocabulary List

1. glitter
2. grubby
3. baggy
4. bony
5. feeble
6. spectacular
7. attractive
8. glossy
9. muscular
10. crooked

3 Build New Vocabulary

The Suffix -y

 Use the words with the suffix -y from the box below to complete each sentence. Write the word in the blank.

mighty	grubby	bony	baggy	glittery
soapy	sleepy	wiggly	giggly	itchy

1. The children were _____ after playing in the muddy puddles.

2. They washed their dirty hands with hot, _____ water.

3. The little girl dressed up in her mother's lacy dress, hat, and _____ necklace.

4. Her brother dressed up in his dad's loose, _____ pants and huge shoes.

5. The thin and _____ boy squeezed through the small trapdoor to the attic.

6. The _____ lioness emerged from under a shady tree.

7. The _____ baby laughed when her father made funny faces.

8. She felt so _____ that she could hardly sit still.

9. The farmer was snoring in his chair—all his hard work had made him _____.

10. Do apes scratch themselves because they are _____?

Score _____ (Top Score 10)   Vocabulary for Appearances • Build New Vocabulary

Word Play

Rhymes

 Write the vocabulary word that best completes each rhyme below.

Clean and Shiny

If your teeth are feeling mossy,

Just brush and floss and they'll be

_____.

Surprise!

I thought my grandma was _____
and weak,
I thought she was quiet, shy, and meek.
But one day at the park, I had quite a surprise,
At first I could not believe my eyes.
There was Grandma skateboarding that day,

Doing _____ tricks, flipping every
which way.
Skateboarding grandmas? It just goes to show,
People surprise you—you just never know!

• •

 Write the vocabulary word that rhymes with each group of words below.

1. chubby, tubby _____

2. bossy, saucy _____

3. shaggy, craggy _____

4. bitter, critter, litter _____

5. pony, phony, macaroni _____

Vocabulary Review

 Review Word Meanings

Read the passage below. Then answer the questions about the boldfaced vocabulary words.

Alice's Adventures in Wonderland

Alice's Adventures in Wonderland is an **enchanting fantasy** story about a girl who follows a rabbit down his rabbit hole and is amazed to find herself in an **unfamiliar,** yet **spectacular,** world. When Alice first sees the rabbit hurrying along and **inspecting** his **glittering** watch without even trying to **conceal** it from her, she wonders at first whether she is truly **conscious** or half-asleep. She makes a **decision** to follow him down his rabbit hole without stopping to **consider** how she will ever get out again.

Now read the following questions. Then completely fill in the bubble of the correct answer.

1. What word has a prefix that means "not"?
   Ⓐ unfamiliar
   Ⓑ inspecting
   Ⓒ conceal

2. Which of the following shows how *conscious* is used in the passage above?
   Ⓐ Alice hoped she was asleep.
   Ⓑ Alice hoped she was able to understand.
   Ⓒ Alice hoped she was fully awake and aware.

3. Which of the following sets are antonyms of *spectacular?*
   Ⓐ enchanting, delightful, wonderful
   Ⓑ common, usual, ordinary
   Ⓒ unfamiliar, logical, grubby

4. Which of the following words means "strange or unknown"?
   Ⓐ unfamiliar
   Ⓑ inspecting
   Ⓒ decision

5. Which of the following sentences is true, according to the passage above?
   Ⓐ The rabbit considered Alice carefully.
   Ⓑ Alice considers and plans her escape.
   Ⓒ Alice does not consider what will happen if she follows the rabbit.

6. Which of the following sentences is true, according to the passage above?
   Ⓐ The rabbit hides a watch.
   Ⓑ The rabbit has no watch.
   Ⓒ The rabbit shows a watch.

2 Review Word Meanings

Read the passage below. Then answer the questions about the boldfaced vocabulary words.

Down the Rabbit Hole

The rabbit hole went along the ground for a while; then it became **crooked** and bent straight down. The hole was not **shallow** but instead very deep and Alice fell down the hole for a long time. Still, the fall was not **harsh.** When Alice landed at the bottom of the hole, she saw a **magnificent** garden through a tiny door. Then she drank a liquid that tasted nice but **transformed** her and made her very small. Next she ate some cake, which made her grow tall like a giant!

Now read the following questions. Then completely fill in the bubble of the correct answer.

1. Which of the following means the opposite of the way *harsh* is used in the passage above?
   Ⓐ scary
   Ⓑ wonderful
   Ⓒ shallow

2. Which word from the passage above means "completely changed"?
   Ⓐ crooked
   Ⓑ transformed
   Ⓒ magnificent

3. Which of the following could also describe the *magnificent* garden?
   Ⓐ wonderful
   Ⓑ crooked
   Ⓒ harsh

4. Which words might Alice use to describe the rabbit hole?
   Ⓐ harsh and shallow
   Ⓑ crooked and magnificent
   Ⓒ deep and crooked

5. Which word means the opposite of *shallow?*
   Ⓐ deep
   Ⓑ narrow
   Ⓒ crooked

6. How was Alice transformed?
   Ⓐ She grew small when she fell.
   Ⓑ She grew into a garden.
   Ⓒ She grew tall when she ate cake.

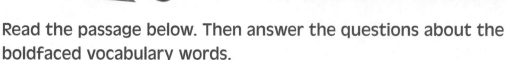

③ Review Word Meanings

Read the passage below. Then answer the questions about the boldfaced vocabulary words.

The Pool of Tears

Alice had grown so large that she began to cry. She **estimated** that she was now nine feet tall! It did not seem **logical** for her to be so very large! Alice could not **conquer** her sadness. She did not feel **heroic.** The ground became **slippery** with her tears, and when she suddenly became small again, she found that the gallons of tears she had shed had **created** a pool in which she was now swimming.

Now read the following questions. Then completely fill in the bubble of the correct answer.

1. If Alice had been *heroic,* what would have been true?
   Ⓐ She would have created a pool with her tears.
   Ⓑ She would have run away.
   Ⓒ She would have conquered her sad feelings.

2. Which of the following defines *logical* as it is used in the passage above?
   Ⓐ making good sense
   Ⓑ aware
   Ⓒ relating to the mind

3. If the suffix *-or* were added to a word from the passage, which word would mean "one who forcefully takes over"?
   Ⓐ creator
   Ⓑ conqueror
   Ⓒ estimator

4. Which word describes Alice guessing that she was nine feet tall?
   Ⓐ created
   Ⓑ estimated
   Ⓒ conquer

5. Which of the following pairs of words has opposite meanings?
   Ⓐ estimated, created
   Ⓑ heroic, fearful
   Ⓒ conquer, fierce

6. Which of the following sentences is true, according to the passage above?
   Ⓐ Alice found a pool and started to cry.
   Ⓑ Alice made a pool because she was crying huge tears.
   Ⓒ Alice cried because the ground was slippery.

4 Review Word Meanings

Read the passage below. Then answer the questions about the boldfaced vocabulary words.

Alice Meets a Mouse

As Alice was swimming in her pool of tears, she saw an **attractive** mouse whose fur had become wet and **glossy** from the water. Alice was not sure whether it was **suitable** for her to speak to a mouse. She used a lot of **concentration** to think about what she should say. Even so, she made a very bad mistake, because she asked if the mouse had seen her cat. The mouse became **hostile** and seemed **fierce** to her because she was so small. The mouse told Alice that she was impossible to **educate.** When Alice saw the White Rabbit run by, she followed him and left the mouse. Alice had many adventures before she left Wonderland.

Now read the following questions. Then completely fill in the bubble of the correct answer.

1. Which of the following pairs of words is used in the passage to describe the mouse?
   - Ⓐ attractive, suitable
   - Ⓑ glossy, suitable
   - Ⓒ fierce, hostile

2. Which words are synonyms for the vocabulary word used to describe the mouse's fur in the passage?
   - Ⓐ wet, glistening, shiny
   - Ⓑ hard, firm, rough
   - Ⓒ thin, bony, weak

3. When Alice thought the mouse was *attractive,* it meant she thought he was _____.
   - Ⓐ good-looking
   - Ⓑ just right
   - Ⓒ well-known

4. Which word means "close attention"?
   - Ⓐ suitable
   - Ⓑ concentration
   - Ⓒ educate

5. Which of the following means the opposite of *hostile*?
   - Ⓐ famous
   - Ⓑ friendly
   - Ⓒ unfriendly

6. Which of the following sentences is true, according to the passage above?
   - Ⓐ The mouse told Alice she could not be kind.
   - Ⓑ The mouse told Alice she could not be taught.
   - Ⓒ The mouse told Alice she could not pay attention.

Vocabulary List

1. **literature**
   (lit′ ər ə chər) *n.*
   artistic writing

2. **extraordinary**
   (ek strôr′ də når ē)
   adj. very special

3. **tragic**
   (trag′ ik) *adj.*
   very sad

4. **paragraph**
   (pâr′ ə graf′) *n.*
   a connected group
   of sentences

5. **fable**
   (fā′ bəl) *n.*
   short story that
   teaches a lesson

6. **comedy**
   (kom′ i dē) *n.*
   a funny story

7. **fascinating**
   (fas′ ə nā ting) *adj.*
   very interesting

8. **sequence**
   (sē′ kwəns) *n.*
   the order of things

9. **respond**
   (ri spond′) *v.*
   to give an answer
   or reaction

10. **conclusion**
    (kən kloo′ zhən) *n.*
    the end or final part

Storytelling Vocabulary

 **Word Meanings**

Order

 Write the vocabulary word that best fits each ordering of words and phrases below.

1. letter, word, sentence, _____

2. beginning, middle, _____

3. sad, sadder, _____

4. ordinary, special, _____

5. boring, interesting, _____

• •

Write the vocabulary word that completes each sentence below.

6. The movie Martha saw last night made her laugh

   because it was a _____.

7. His huge bookshelf was built to store his collection

   of _____.

8. In a debate, one person gives an argument and
   another person has a chance to

   _____.

9. Aesop's _____ are famous stories
   that teach lessons, but no one is sure whether Aesop
   really wrote them all.

10. In the book *The Lion, the Witch, and the Wardrobe,*
    the character Aslan changed the

    _____ of time and made it go

    backward.

Score _____ (Top Score 10)   Storytelling Vocabulary • Word Meanings

② Reference Skills
Phonetic Spellings

Write the vocabulary word that best matches each phonetic spelling and fits in the sentence.

1. "The Lion and the Mouse" is a

   _____ (fas′ ə nā ting) story.

2. This work of _____ (lit′ ər ə chər) is more than 2,000 years old.

3. In this _____ (fā′ bəl) by Aesop, a lion captures a mouse. The helpless mouse talks the lion into letting him go by promising to help the lion.

4. The lion finally does _____ (ri spond′) by allowing the mouse to go free.

5. It is _____ (ek stror′ də när ē) that later, the tiny mouse is able to help the mighty lion.

6. In the _____ (sē′ kwəns) of the story, the lion gets trapped in a net, and the mouse chews a hole through it to set the lion free.

7. This _____ (kən kloo′ zhən) of the fable proves the old saying, "No act of kindness, no matter how small, is ever wasted."

8. Although the story is not much longer than a

   _____ (par′ ə graf′), it has helped many people learn the importance of kindness.

Vocabulary List

1. literature
2. extraordinary
3. tragic
4. paragraph
5. fable
6. comedy
7. fascinating
8. sequence
9. respond
10. conclusion

3 Build New Vocabulary

Context Clues

Read the passages below. Use context clues to figure out what each underlined word means. Then write the vocabulary word that means the same thing.

1. There is an African story about two boys who lived next to each other. They were very good friends. Another boy decided to play a trick on them. This trickster made himself a very special coat. One half of this <u>phenomenal</u> coat was red, the other was blue.

   _____

2. The trickster wore this coat and walked between their houses. He made noise so they would notice him. Each friend looked up and stared. The beautiful coat was <u>engaging</u>—its color was so interesting.

   _____

3. One friend said, "That blue coat was so beautiful." The other <u>rejoined</u>, "It was red, not blue." The friends argued about the coat's color. Soon they were yelling

   with anger. _____

4. The trickster came back and laughed. Then the friends saw that the coat was both blue and red. They were mad at the trickster. But the trickster said, "Do not be mad at me. You each saw something true. You were fighting because you each saw my coat from your own point of view." This short <u>yarn</u> teaches that different opinions are important.

   _____

4 Word Play

Using Descriptive Words

Choose a descriptive word from the box to replace each commonly used boldfaced word in the sentences below.

fascinating	mightier	conclusion	freezing
responded	fable	sequence	fiery

1. In another **story** _____ by Aesop, the North Wind and the Sun were having an argument about whose power was **stronger** _____.

2. When they saw a man wearing a coat outside, they decided to see who could make the man remove his coat. The North Wind blew very hard and was

   very cold _____, but the man

   only **reacted** _____ by holding more tightly onto his coat.

3. Next in the **order** _____ of events was the Sun's turn.

4. So the Sun turned his **hot** _____ rays on the man.

5. What happened next was **interesting**

   _____. The man became so hot that he took off his coat.

6. The **end** _____ of this tale shows that often, force is not the best way to get someone to do something.

Vocabulary List

1. **dense**
   (dens) *adj.*
   thick; tightly packed
   together

2. **bustling**
   (bus´ əl ing) *adj.*
   moving quickly and
   excitedly

3. **mossy**
   (mô´ sē) *adj.*
   covered with soft,
   small green plants

4. **murky**
   (mûr´ kē) *adj.*
   dark and cloudy

5. **stale**
   (stāl) *adj.*
   no longer fresh

6. **rustle**
   (rus´ əl) *v.*
   to make soft,
   fluttering sounds

7. **chapel**
   (chap´ əl) *n.*
   little church

8. **tavern**
   (tav´ ərn) *n.*
   small hotel or inn

9. **cobblestoned**
   (kob´ əl stōn) *adj.*
   made of small,
   round stones

10. **arch**
    (ärch) *n.*
    curved doorway

Story Settings

① Word Meanings

Descriptions

 Write the vocabulary word that best fits each description below.

1. The guests blew bubbles as the bride and groom exited the small building. _____

2. Somewhere from within the deep, dense wood came a soft, fluttering sound. _____

3. A spider had spun a web in the curved doorway.
   _____

4. After the hurricane, the ocean was so cloudy with sand that we could no longer see the reef while snorkeling. _____

5. The rocks were covered with a soft, green growth.
   _____

6. We stopped at the little inn and rented a room for the night. _____

7. The town was filled with people hurrying along the cobblestoned streets. _____

8. The old loaf of bread was tough and chewy.
   _____

② Reference Skills

Words with Multiple Meanings

Read the dictionary entries and the sentences below. Choose the definition that best matches each underlined word. Then write the part of speech and the number of the definition you chose for each sentence.

---

arch *n.* **1.** a curved structure, such as a doorway or window **2.** the middle of the foot that is raised up in a curve
—*v.* **1.** to form something in the shape of a curve

bustle *v.* **1.** to move quickly and noisily
—*n.* **1.** a pad in the back of a skirt to add fullness

stale *adj.* **1.** no longer fresh **2.** something that has become boring

---

1. The old joke was so <u>stale</u> that when Jacob told it, no one laughed. _____

2. Cats <u>arch</u> their backs when they are angry.

   _____

3. Long ago it was the fashion for women to wear <u>bustles</u> under their skirts. _____

4. The Arch of Triumph in Paris, France, is one of the world's most famous <u>arches</u>.

   _____

5. Squirrels <u>bustle</u> about in the fall gathering nuts for the winter. _____

Vocabulary List

1. dense
2. bustling
3. mossy
4. murky
5. stale
6. rustle
7. chapel
8. tavern
9. cobblestoned
10. arch

 3 Build New Vocabulary

Comparatives and Superlatives

Add the *-er* and *-est* endings to the vocabulary words below to form comparative and superlative adjectives.

1. murky – *y* + *ier* = _____

2. murky – *y* + *iest* = _____

3. dense + *er* = _____

4. dense + *est* = _____

5. mossy – *y* + *ier* = _____

6. mossy – *y* + *iest* = _____

 Complete each sentence below using the correct comparative or superlative adjective that you formed above.

7. The rainstorm stirred up the mud in the pond and made the water even _____ than it was before.

8. Rain forests have so many trees and other plants growing closely together that they are the _____ forests on Earth.

9. Most moss grows in the shade, so stones in a forest are _____ than stones in a desert.

10. The fog was the _____ fog we had ever seen—it was like being inside a cloud.

4  **Word Play**

Rhymes

Complete each rhyme below using the vocabulary word that best fits.

1. A joke that is old,
and many times told,

   is as _____ as bread that is
   covered with mold.

2. The rocks that once were glossy,

   have now turned green and _____.

3. "It's too _____ in the wood,"
said Red Riding Hood.
"This is not at all good,
I can't see as I should."

4. She wanted to build a new fence
Through the forest that was very _____.
She tried to use skis
To chop down the trees
Till she realized that didn't make sense.

5. We march
Through the_____
Toward adventures ahead!
(Too bad
I'd be glad
Just to go back to bed.)

Vocabulary List

1. **foundation**
   (foun dā´ shən) n.
   base or support

2. **frame**
   (frām) n.
   bones of a building

3. **concrete**
   (kon´ krēt) n.
   cement mixture

4. **gravel**
   (grav´ əl) n.
   small rocks

5. **blueprint**
   (bloo´ print) n.
   a drawn plan for
   a building

6. **timber**
   (tim´ bər) n.
   wood for
   building with

7. **shingles**
   (shing´ gəlz) n.
   thin, overlapping
   strips for roofs

8. **platform**
   (plat´ form) n.
   raised floor

9. **pane**
   (pān) n.
   sheet of glass

10. **plastic**
    (plas´ tik) n.
    humanmade,
    bendable material

Construction Vocabulary

 1 **Word Meanings**

Sentence Completion

 Write the vocabulary word that correctly completes each sentence below.

1. Before a house is built, the designer makes a plan called a ___blueprint___.

2. The ___foundation___, or base, is built first because it supports the rest of the house.

3. Often, the base is made of _____, which becomes very hard when it dries.

4. Many houses are built with brick, stone, or ___concrete___.

5. The ___frame___ of a house is like the bones of a human body.

6. Some houses have a raised ___platform___ attached outside, called a deck.

7. The water pipes in a house can be made of metal or ___plastic___ because both are bendable.

8. ___Shingles___ prevent water from coming through the roof of a house because they overlap.

9. The front door of a house sometimes has a ___pane___ of glass so that the owner can see who is at the door.

10. A path made of pieces of ___gravel___ can add a nice touch to a garden.

② Reference Skills

The Base Word *form*

 Use the words from the box to complete each sentence below.

---

formless *adj.* **1.** having no shape or form

formal *adj.* **1.** proper or stiff in behavior

platform *n.* **1.** a raised floor

form *v.* **1.** to give something a shape

format *n.* **1.** the way a book or magazine is put together

---

1. The _____ of the book did not make sense to me.

2. When water becomes a gas, it has no form and is therefore _____.

3. At a concert, the band will often stand on a _____ so the audience can see them.

4. Someone whose actions always follow the most proper form is a _____ person.

5. Potters are people who _____ clay into bowls and sculptures.

6. A _____ attached to the front of a house is called a porch.

Vocabulary List

1. *foundation*

2. *frame*

3. *concrete*

4. *gravel*

5. *blueprint*

6. *timber*

7. *shingles*

8. *platform*

9. *pane*

10. *plastic*

3 Build New Vocabulary

Compound Words

 Write the compound word from the box below that matches each clue.

timberwolf	timberland	windowpane
mailcarrier	entranceway	framework
taxpayer	wastepaper	blueprint
wasteland		

1. a person who pays a tax _____

2. paper to throw away _____

3. a person who delivers letters _____

4. a single sheet of glass _____

5. land covered with trees _____

6. an opening into a house _____

7. a print that shows plans _____

8. land on which nothing can grow _____

9. a doglike animal that lives in the forest _____

10. a structure that is a frame for something _____

 **Word Play**

Answering Questions

 Write *Yes* or *No* to answer each question below.

1. Could you make a *blueprint* using *panes?* _____

2. Could you make a *frame* using *timber?* _____

3. Could you make a *foundation* using a *frame?*

_____

4. Could you make a *foundation* using *concrete?*

_____

5. Could you make a *driveway* using *gravel?* _____

6. Could you make *pipes* using *plastic?* _____

7. Could you make *panes* using *timber?* _____

8. Could you make a *platform* using *timber?* _____

9. Could you make *concrete* using *shingles?* _____

10. Could you make a *blueprint* using *gravel?* _____

11. Could you make a *blueprint* for a *frame?* _____

12. Could *concrete* become *timber?* _____

Vocabulary List

1. **primitive**
   (prim´ i tiv) *adj.*
   relating to an early
   stage

2. **generation**
   (jen ə rā´ shən) *n.*
   people born about
   the same time

3. **prehistoric**
   (prē his tor´ ik) *adj.*
   happening before
   history was written

4. **modern**
   (mod´ ərn) *adj.*
   of the present time

5. **era**
   (er´ ə) *n.*
   period of time in
   history

6. **old-fashioned**
   (ōld´ fash´ ənd) *adj.*
   keeping old ideas

7. **amateur**
   (am´ ə chər) *n.*
   a beginner

8. **up-to-date**
   (up´ too dāt´) *adj.*
   having the most
   recent facts

9. **restore**
   (ri stor´) *v.*
   to bring back

10. **fad**
    (fad) *n.*
    short-lived fashion
    or interest

"Old and New" Vocabulary

 **Word Meanings**

Definitions

 Write each vocabulary word next to its correct definition below.

1. a fashion or interest that lasts for a short time

   _____

2. related to the present time

   _____

3. to bring back to an earlier state or condition

   _____

4. a person who is unskilled; a beginner

   _____

5. using or having the most recent facts

   _____

6. having old or outdated ideas and ways of doing

   things _____

7. a period of time in history _____

8. relating to an early stage in human development

   _____

9. a group of people who were born at about the

   same time _____

10. happening before history was written

    _____

② Reference Skills

Hyphenated Compound Words

Each of the compound words in the box should have a hyphen to separate the smaller words. Write each compound word next to its definition and add the hyphen, or hyphens, where they belong. Use a dictionary if you need help.

allpurpose	eventempered	handmedown	oneway
oldfashioned	selfportrait	uptodate	wellsuited

1. _____ likes to use old ways of doing things

2. _____ able to be used for many different things

3. _____ having the most recent facts

4. _____ a picture of a person painted by that same person

5. _____ fitting something or someone very well

6. _____ calm; not easily disturbed

7. _____ able to go in only one direction

8. _____ something that has been used and then given to someone else

• •

 Think About It

Compound words often start out hyphenated, but eventually the hyphen disappears. What compound word can you think of that has no hyphen but might have had one long ago?

Vocabulary List

1. *primitive*

2. *generation*

3. *prehistoric*

4. *modern*

5. *era*

6. *old-fashioned*

7. *amateur*

8. *up-to-date*

9. *restore*

10. *fad*

3 Build New Vocabulary

The Prefix *pre-*

 Add the prefix *pre-* to each word below.

1. pre + pay = _____, meaning "to pay before an item is received"

2. pre + historic = _____, meaning "something that lived or happened before history was written"

3. pre + judge = _____, meaning "to form an idea about something before knowing all the facts"

4. pre + teen = _____, meaning "a person who is eleven or twelve years old"

5. pre + assembled = _____, meaning "already put together"

• •

 Complete each sentence below using the correct word that you formed above.

6. We do not know what color dinosaurs were because they were _____ animals.

7. The students had to _____ for their concert tickets.

8. Usually, a _____ is in middle school.

9. Some bikes come _____, while others have to be put together.

10. People who _____ others aren't being fair.

Score _____ (Top Score 10)   "Old and New" Vocabulary • Build New Vocabulary

Word Play

Alliteration

Complete each alliterative sentence below with the vocabulary word that best fits.

1. Plain people like private, _____ places.

2. _____ artists are arranging apples as an artwork.

3. Many _____ machines make making meals less messy.

4. A _____ of junior officers just jetted off to join the general.

5. Flip-flops for the feet are a funny fashion

   _____.

6. _____ people painted primitive pictures.

7. Rachel will _____ the rickety, rotten railing.

8. Uncle's ugly umbrella was unfortunately not

   _____.

9. The _____ officer wore an odd, outdated overcoat.

10. When Elizabeth ruled England, it was the Elizabethan

    _____.

Time Vocabulary

1. **annual**
   (anˊ ū əl) *adj.*
   once a year

2. **temporary**
   (temˊ pə rârē) *adj.*
   lasting for a short
   time

3. **eve**
   (ēv) *n.*
   the evening before
   a special day

4. **hourly**
   (ourˊ lē) *adv.*
   once every sixty
   minutes

5. **momentarily**
   (mōˊ mən târ i lē)
   adv.
   very soon; in a
   minute

6. **twilight**
   (twīˊ līt) *n.*
   time just after sunset

7. **occasional**
   (ə kāˊ zhə nəl) *adj.*
   happening once in
   a while

8. **lately**
   (lātˊ lē) *adv.*
   not long ago

9. **afterward**
   (afˊ tər wərd) *adv.*
   at a later time

10. **everlasting**
    (ev ər lasˊ ting) *adj.*
    lasting forever

1 **Word Meanings**

Word Lines

 Write the related words or phrases from each box below in order.

1. | twilight | noon | afternoon |

   dawn, _____

2. | annual | weekly |

   hourly, _____, monthly, _____

3. | occasional | often |

   never, _____, always

4. | Eve | Day |

   New Year's _____, New Year's_____,
   January 2nd

• •

 Circle the vocabulary word that completes each sentence below.

   In the fable "The Grasshopper and the Ant," Grasshopper thinks that summer will be *(everlasting/ lately),* so he has not saved food for the winter. Ant, however, has saved food lately because he knows that summer is *(afterward/ temporary)* and will not last forever. Grasshopper makes fun of Ant momentarily, but *(afterward/ occasional)* he learns that it is wise to plan for the future.

② Reference Skills

Definitions

Write each vocabulary word next to its correct definition below. Use a dictionary if you need help.

1. the time just after the sun has set

   _____

2. very soon; in just a minute _____

3. happening once in a while _____

4. happening once every twelve months

   _____

5. not very long ago _____

6. the evening before a special day

   _____

7. lasting for a short time _____

8. going on in time forever _____

9. at a later time _____

10. happening once every sixty minutes

    _____

Vocabulary List

1. annual
2. temporary
3. eve
4. hourly
5. momentarily
6. twilight
7. occasional
8. lately
9. afterward
10. everlasting

3 Build New Vocabulary

Abbreviations

Study each numbered abbreviation below. Then write the word or phrase from the box that matches each abbreviation.

annual	as soon as possible	contribution
division	hour	minute
literature	miles per hour	temporary
second		

1. div.   _division_
2. lit.   _literature_
3. ASAP   _as soon as possible._
4. hr.   _hour_
5. ann.   _annual_
6. MPH   _miles per hour_
7. temp.   _temporary_
8. contrib.   _contribute_
9. sec.   _second_
10. min.   _minute_

Think About It

Some abbreviations stand for words from other languages. Look in a dictionary to discover what French words the abbreviation *RSVP* stands for.

Word Play

Words Inside Words

Write the vocabulary word that contains all of the words in each numbered group below and matches the clue given.

1. as, sting, eve (It goes on and on and on . . .)

   _____

2. tar, omen, me, men, mom (Just a minute)

   _____

3. as, on, ion (Oh, we could do it once in a while)

   _____

4. our, hour (The number sixty is the key)

   _____

5. ate, late (Yesterday happened at this time)

   _____

6. light (This is when the sun goes out)

   _____

7. ward, war, aft (Can't I do it later?)

   _____

8. temp (This page didn't take long)

   _____

. . . .

Think About It

Which vocabulary word has no other words hidden inside it?

Vocabulary Review

1 **Review Word Meanings**

Read the passage below. Then answer the questions about the boldfaced vocabulary words.

Fables

Fables are an **old-fashioned** form of **literature,** but many of them are still **fascinating** to people of the **modern era.** Even though a fable might be only one **paragraph** long, its **conclusion** teaches a lesson that remains **up-to-date** for every **generation.**

Now read the following questions. Then completely fill in the bubble of the correct answer.

1. Which word in the passage above is a hyphenated compound word that means "relating to old ways or ideas"?
   Ⓐ old-fashioned
   Ⓑ modern era
   Ⓒ up-to-date

2. Which word in the passage above completes the order of the following sequence?
   beginning, middle, _____
   Ⓐ paragraph
   Ⓑ modern
   Ⓒ conclusion

3. Which of the following is true according to the passage above?
   Ⓐ people still learn from fables
   Ⓑ people hate fables
   Ⓒ people only learned from fables long ago

4. Which of the following sets includes only words that can be grouped under the heading *Literature?*
   Ⓐ fables, stories, poems
   Ⓑ word, sentence, paragraph
   Ⓒ paintings, movies, books

5. Which of the following is a definition of *generation?*
   Ⓐ a period of time in history
   Ⓑ something that belongs to the present time
   Ⓒ a group of people who were all born at about the same time

6. Which of the following pairs includes only synonyms of *fascinating?*
   Ⓐ extraordinary, everlasting
   Ⓑ famous, fantasy
   Ⓒ enchanting, interesting

② Review Word Meanings

Read the passage below. Then answer the questions about the boldfaced vocabulary words.

The Town Mouse and the Country Mouse

In one famous fable, a mouse who lived in a **bustling** town asked his country cousin to dinner. The town mouse promised his cousin an **extraordinary** dinner that he would remember forever **afterward.** The next day, at **twilight,** the country cousin left his home and set off along the **cobblestoned** road of the town. He met his town cousin under the **arch** of the **tavern** in which the town mouse lived.

Now read the following questions. Then completely fill in the bubble of the correct answer.

1. Which of the following pairs includes two correct definitions of *arch?*
   Ⓐ "to form in the shape of a curve" and "a pane of glass"
   Ⓑ "to form in the shape of a curve" and "a curved doorway or window"
   Ⓒ "to form in the shape of a curve" and "to make a road with small stones"

2. Which of the following is a definition of *twilight* as it is used in the passage above?
   Ⓐ happening now and then
   Ⓑ the evening before a special day
   Ⓒ the time just after the sun has set

3. Which of the following is a description of *bustling?*
   Ⓐ The city street was made of thousands of small, smooth stones.
   Ⓑ The city street was filled with people talking and hurrying from one place to another.
   Ⓒ The city street had a chapel and a tavern on the corner.

4. Which of the following means the same as *afterward?*
   Ⓐ late
   Ⓑ later
   Ⓒ lately

5. Which of the following relates to the meaning of *tavern?*
   Ⓐ The travelers stopped at the small inn to eat dinner and rest for the night.
   Ⓑ The wedding guests walked up the path to the small church.
   Ⓒ The foundation of the building was made of concrete.

③ Review Word Meanings

Read the passage below. Then answer the questions about the boldfaced vocabulary words.

The Town Dinner

The town mouse led his cousin under the **foundation** of the tavern and into a large dining room. Food had fallen **lately** from the tables and it was scattered all over the floor. Even though the food was **stale,** it was still a feast for the mice.

But the country mouse's pleasure was only **temporary,** for he was sure that he heard the sound of a cat. The town mouse paused **momentarily** and told his cousin not to worry. And the town mouse continued to eat.

However, the country mouse could not **restore** his happy mood, for he kept hearing the purring of the cat. He was afraid of a **tragic** ending to his visit.

Now read the following questions. Then completely fill in the bubble of the correct answer.

1. Which vocabulary word in the passage above means "very soon"?
   (A) lately
   (B) temporary
   (C) momentarily

2. Which of the following pairs of words have opposite meanings?
   (A) temporary, restore
   (B) tragic, happy
   (C) momentarily, stale

3. What does *restore* mean in the passage above?
   (A) to give an answer to his feelings
   (B) to bring back his happy feelings
   (C) to redo his happy feelings

4. Which word in the passage above means "lasting only a short while"?
   (A) tragic
   (B) temporary
   (C) sequence

5. Which word in the passage above means "no longer fresh or interesting"?
   (A) stale
   (B) temporary
   (C) tragic

6. Which of the following is true according to the passage above?
   (A) The town mouse lived on a roof.
   (B) The town mouse lived inside a wall.
   (C) The town mouse lived under the floor.

4 Review Word Meanings

Read the passage below. Then answer the questions about the boldfaced vocabulary words.

Back to the Country

"Goodbye, Cousin," said the country mouse.

"But where are you going?" the town mouse asked. "We haven't finished our dinner."

"I'm going back to my home under my tree, inside the **mossy** ground in the **dense** woods," **responded** the country mouse. "I might have an **occasional** scare at home when an owl happens to fly overhead," he continued, "my home may not be built out of **timber** or have **shingles** on its roof, and my food is much more **primitive** than yours. But I can't stand this **everlasting** fear that a cat will catch me."

And the country mouse went home.

Now read the following questions. Then completely fill in the bubble of the correct answer.

1. Which of the following is a description of *primitive?*
   Ⓐ The town mouse lived in a modern tavern that served spectacular food.
   Ⓑ The country mouse lived under a tree and ate plain food.
   Ⓒ The country mouse didn't like the stale food at the town mouse's tavern.

2. According to the passage above, which of the following sentences is true?
   Ⓐ The woods are noisy.
   Ⓑ The woods are wide-open.
   Ⓒ The woods are thick.

3. If a forest is *dense*, it _____ .
   Ⓐ is very green and mossy
   Ⓑ has many open spaces in it
   Ⓒ has many trees and other plants growing close together

4. Which of the following means the same as *responded?*
   Ⓐ laughed
   Ⓑ answered
   Ⓒ asked

5. Which of the following does *not* mean the same as *everlasting?*
   Ⓐ occasional
   Ⓑ forever
   Ⓒ always

1. **profit**
(prof´ it) *n.*
money that is
gained

2. **wages**
(wā´ jəz) *n.*
payment for work

3. **account**
(ə kount´) *n.*
written record
of money

4. **thrifty**
(thrif´ tē) *adj.*
very careful with
money

5. **bill**
(bil) *n.*
written record of
money due

6. **donate**
(dō´ nāt) *v.*
to give freely

7. **bankrupt**
(bangk´ rupt) *adj.*
unable to pay
money owed

8. **expense**
(ek spens´) *n.*
money spent

9. **lend**
(lend) *v.*
to let someone
borrow

10. **afford**
(ə ford´) *v.*
to be able to buy

"Money" Vocabulary

 1 **Word Meanings**

Sentence Completion

 Write the vocabulary word that correctly completes each sentence below.

1. Lindsey's neighbor pays her _____ of $5 an hour to cut his grass.

2. The cost of gasoline for her lawn mower is the only _____ Lindsey has for her job.

3. Every month, Lindsey gives her neighbor a _____ that shows how much money he owes her.

4. Lindsey subtracts the amount of money she spent on gasoline from the amount that her neighbor paid her to find out what her _____ is.

5. Lindsey keeps an _____ of the amount of money she earns and spends.

6. Lindsey couldn't afford a new baseball glove, so her mother agreed to _____ her $20 so she could buy it.

7. After she pays her mother back, Lindsey plans to _____ $5 to the food bank, which gives food to people who can't afford it.

8. Lindsey will probably never go _____ because she is learning how to be thrifty and how to earn and manage money.

2 Reference Skills

Dictionary Phrases

Read the phrases in the box below. Then complete each sentence by writing the phrase that best fits.

Definitions

- **on account of** because of
- **on no account** never
- **on my account** for one or to help one
- **to account for** to explain the reason for
- **take into account** to allow for or consider
- **fit the bill** to be just what is needed
- **a clean bill of health** a good report

---

1. _____ will I ever swim in the lake in December again. I nearly froze!

2. A good speaker will always _____ the age and interests of his or her listeners.

3. Scott hadn't eaten since breakfast, so the sandwiches really _____ .

4. When we arrived at school ten minutes late, our teacher asked us _____ our lateness.

5. The school closed early _____ the storm warning.

6. Please don't feel that you have to stay and clean up _____ .

Vocabulary List

1. profit
2. wages
3. account
4. thrifty
5. bill
6. donate
7. bankrupt
8. expense
9. lend
10. afford

3 Build New Vocabulary

The Suffix -able

 Add the suffix -able to each word below to form an adjective that matches the definition.

1. profit + able = _____: able to make money

2. reason + able = _____: making good sense

3. account + able = _____: responsible for

4. consider + able = _____: great in amount

5. afford + able = _____: able to be bought

• •

 Complete each sentence below by writing the correct adjective that you formed above.

6. Every member of the group is

_____ for the project to raise money for new playground toys.

7. It is _____ for each member of the group to have certain jobs to do.

8. It takes a _____ amount of cooperation to complete a group project.

9. If the group project is _____, the students will have enough money for the new playground toys.

10. The students will go to several stores to find the

most _____ toys.

Score _____ (Top Score 10)   "Money" Vocabulary • Build New Vocabulary

4 Word Play

Answering Questions

Write *Yes* or *No* to tell whether each relationship in the questions below is possible.

1. Could a person write down *expenses* in an *account?*

   _____

2. Could a person *donate* an *expense* to a food bank?

   _____

3. Could a person who is *bankrupt afford* to buy a new house? _____

4. Could a person *donate* some of her *wages* to a food bank? _____

5. Could a person who gets *wages* make a *profit?*

   _____

6. Could a *thrifty* person *save* money?

   _____

7. Could a person *lend* another person some of his *expenses?* _____

8. Could a person use her *profit* to *pay* for food?

   _____

9. Could a *thrifty* person keep an *account?*

   _____

10. Could a person's *expenses* make him *bankrupt?*

   _____

Vocabulary List

1. **colonel**
(kûr′ nəl) *n.*
leader of soldiers

2. **lawyer**
(lô′ yər) *n.*
speaker in court for another person

3. **author**
(ô′ thər) *n.*
writer of stories and poems

4. **carpenter**
(kär′ pən tər) *n.*
builder of wooden things

5. **mechanic**
(mi kan′ ik) *n.*
one who fixes machines

6. **engineer**
(en jə nēr′) *n.*
creator of machines

7. **veterinarian**
(vet′ ər ə nâr′ ē ən)
n. animal doctor

8. **director**
(di rek′ tər) *n.*
one in charge of actors

9. **pharmacist**
(fär′ mə sist) *n.*
one who prepares and sells medicines

10. **architect**
(är′ ki tekt′) *n.*
person who designs buildings

Vocabulary for Careers

1 Word Meanings

Definitions

 Write the vocabulary word that is defined in each sentence below.

1. A _____ is a person who has a license to prepare and sell medicine that a doctor has requested for a patient.

2. A _____ works on and fixes machines such as cars.

3. A _____ speaks for another person in a court of law.

4. A _____ is a person who oversees and leads the actors and other people working on a play, movie, or television show.

5. An _____ writes stories, poems, and plays.

6. A _____ uses wood to build things such as chairs, tables, and cupboards.

7. An _____ plans how to build machines.

8. A _____ is a leader in charge of a large group of soldiers.

9. An _____ plans and makes drawings of buildings.

10. A _____ is a doctor for animals.

② Reference Skills

Guide Words

Write the vocabulary word that would appear on the same page as each set of guide words below.

1. coal/crate   _____

2. lasting/layer   _____

3. arrive/authority   _____

4. carol/catch   _____

5. measure/medal   _____

6. engage/enjoy   _____

7. version/vex   _____

8. acquire/assure   _____

Complete each sentence below with the vocabulary word that best fits.

9. The _____ spread out her blueprints on the table and explained the design of the building.

10. In the army, a _____ is in charge of soldiers, but he or she must follow the general.

11. In the past a _____ only sold medicine, but now this person gives patients advice and helps doctors take care of their patients.

12. The _____ rubbed rough sandpaper on the chair leg to make it smooth.

Vocabulary List

1. colonel
2. lawyer
3. author
4. carpenter
5. mechanic
6. engineer
7. veterinarian
8. director
9. pharmacist
10. architect

3 Build New Vocabulary

Base Word Families

Write each word from the box below next to its correct definition. Then write the vocabulary word that belongs to the same base word family. Use a dictionary if you need help.

carpentry	veterinary	mechanical
architecture	engineering	pharmacy
direction	authored	

1. wrote

   _____   _____

2. a store where medicine is sold

   _____   _____

3. relating to the workings of a machine

   _____   _____

4. the career of designing buildings

   _____   _____

5. relating to making animals well

   _____   _____

6. the career of building things with wood

   _____   _____

7. an order or instruction

   _____   _____

8. the career of designing machines

   _____   _____

Word Play

Riddles

Write the vocabulary word that answers each riddle below.

1. I read a play and choose actors. I tell them where to stand and help them understand the play. Who am I?

   _____

2. I am a leader of many soldiers. I make decisions and

   give orders. Who am I? _____

3. I develop ideas for new buildings. I make drawings of what the buildings will look like. Who am I?

   _____

4. People bring their furry friends to see me, and I make sure they stay healthy. Who am I?

   _____

5. I choose pieces of wood and use tools to shape them. I build beautiful furniture. Who am I?

   _____

6. I work with my hands. I use tools to fix metal things.

   Who am I? _____

7. I invent new machines. I make drawings of what the machines will look like and what parts they will have.

   Who am I? _____

8. I do a lot of speaking for other people, and I give

   them advice. Who am I? _____

1. **pinch**
   (pinch) *n.*
   very small amount

2. **sum**
   (sum) *n.*
   total of addition

3. **maximum**
   (mak´ sə məm) *adj.*
   greatest possible

4. **partially**
   (pär´ shəlē) *adv.*
   not completely
   finished

5. **numerous**
   (nōō´ mər əs) *adj.*
   many

6. **unit**
   (ū´ nit) *n.*
   a single thing or part

7. **duo**
   (dōō´ ō) *n.*
   two people or things

8. **trio**
   (trē´ ō) *n.*
   three people
   or things

9. **scale**
   (skāl) *n.*
   a tool that weighs
   things

10. **tally**
    (tal´ ē) *v.*
    to keep count
    of something

Vocabulary for Amounts

① Word Meanings

Sentence Completion

 Write the vocabulary word that correctly completes each sentence below.

1. The two sisters made a beautiful _____ as they entered the room for their birthday party.

2. The guests brought _____ presents for the twins.

3. As the party began, three of the girls' friends formed a _____ at the front of the room and sang "Happy Birthday."

4. The girls' brother was in charge of the games, so he got out a pencil and paper to _____ the scores of the guests.

5. For the memory game, the _____, or highest, score possible was 20 points.

6. The guest who had the highest _____ of points for all the games put together won an extra prize.

7. The guests had to guess the weight of a jar of pennies before it was weighed on a _____.

8. The girls' mother used two cups of flour, one cup of sugar, a pinch of cinnamon, and one unit of butter to make cookies. Even when the cookies were only _____ baked and still in the oven, they gave off a wonderful smell.

2 Reference Skills

Words with Multiple Meanings

Read the dictionary entries below. Then write the part of speech and the number of the definition of the underlined word in each sentence.

---

pinch *v.* **1.** to squeeze between the thumb and forefinger **2.** to be very careful with money; *n.* **1.** a very small amount **2.** a hardship or difficulty

scale *n.* **1.** a tool used to weigh an object **2.** a series of musical tones that go up or down in pitch **3.** one of the flat pieces of the outer covering of animals such as snakes and fish; *v.* **1.** to weigh **2.** to climb up

---

1. To <u>pinch</u> pennies means to be very careful about

   spending money. _____

2. Some people think that snakes are slimy, but their
   <u>scales</u> are actually smooth and dry.

   _____

3. Mount Everest, which is the highest mountain in the
   world, was first <u>scaled</u> by a person in 1953.

   _____

4. On St. Patrick's Day it is customary to <u>pinch</u> people
   who are not wearing the color green.

   _____

5. Practicing <u>scales</u> is a good way to warm up before

   playing a song on the piano. _____

Vocabulary List

1. pinch
2. sum
3. maximum
4. partially
5. numerous
6. unit
7. duo
8. trio
9. scale
10. tally

3 Build New Vocabulary

Restatement
Context Clues

Use context clues to figure out what the underlined words in the sentences mean. Write the vocabulary word that means the same thing in the blank.

1. Throughout history people have had many different ways of measuring things. During the Middle Ages there were so many ways to count and <u>calculate</u> things that they were not the same from town to

   town! _____

2. At that time the distance of a furlong meant the <u>utmost</u>, or farthest, distance that an ox could pull a plow before it was so tired that it had to rest.

   _____

3. One inch was defined as the total, <u>aggregate</u> length of three good-sized grains of barley laid end to end.

   _____

4. If a recipe from the middle ages said to use a <u>brace</u> of pheasants, it meant that you should cook two

   birds that had long tails. _____

5. Eventually countries agreed on ways to measure amounts. But there are still many <u>various</u> ways to measure things throughout the world.

   _____

 **4** **Word Play**

Crossword Puzzle

Complete the crossword puzzle below using the vocabulary words.

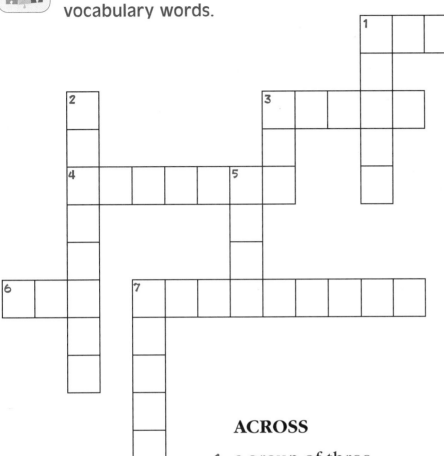

ACROSS

1. a group of three
3. a tool for weighing things
4. the greatest possible
6. two
7. not completely finished

DOWN

1. to keep a count
2. many
3. total of addition
5. a single person or thing
7. a very small amount

Vocabulary List

1. **brittle**
   (brit′ əl) *adj.*
   stiff and easily broken

2. **damp**
   (damp) *adj.*
   a little bit wet

3. **misshapen**
   (mis shā′ pən) *adj.*
   badly formed

4. **lean**
   (lēn) *adj.*
   thin

5. **fragile**
   (fraj′ əl) *adj.*
   frail; needing special care

6. **submerge**
   (səb mûrj′) *v.*
   to put under water

7. **firm**
   (fûrm) *adj.*
   solid and strong

8. **rumple**
   (rum′ pəl) *v.*
   to mess up by wrinkling

9. **flexible**
   (flek′ sə bəl) *adj.*
   easily bent or changed

10. **inflate**
    (in flāt′) *v.*
    to fill with air

Physical Conditions

① Word Meanings

Synonyms and Antonyms

 Write the vocabulary word that matches each synonym and antonym below.

Synonym	Antonym	Vocabulary Word
1. delicate	strong	_____
2. breakable	flexible	_____
3. thin	wide	_____
4. wrinkle	smooth	_____
5. moist	dry	_____
6. fill	deflate	_____
7. sink	emerge	_____
8. solid	flimsy	_____
9. bendable	brittle	_____
10. deformed	perfect	_____

 Match each vocabulary word below with its definition.

11. ____ rumple   **A.** thin

12. ____ lean   **B.** to make something wrinkled

13. ____ brittle   **C.** wrongly formed

14. ____ submerge   **D.** to cover with water

15. ____ misshapen   **E.** easily snapped or broken

② Reference Skills

Base Word Families

Complete the passage below by circling the words in parentheses that complete each sentence. (**Hint:** Use the definitions in the box to help you.)

> **rumple**: to mess up by wrinkling
>
> **rumpled**: something that has been messed up by wrinkling
>
> **firm**: solid and strong
>
> **firmly**: not changing
>
> **inflatable**: able to be filled with air
>
> **inflate**: to cause to swell by filling with air
>
> **inflater**: a tool that fills something with gas or air

The First Balloon Flight Around the World

On March 20, 1999, Bertrand Piccard and Brian Jones became the first people to travel around the world in a balloon. They flew nonstop for nearly 20 days and traveled 29,055 miles. The balloon was loose and *(rumpled/firmly)* before they filled it with air, but once they *(inflater/inflated)* it, the two men followed the winds east around the world.

They kept the balloon 36,000 feet above the sea by continuing to fill the *(inflatable/inflate)* balloon with hot air from a gas heater. Before the *(inflate/inflater)* was invented in 1960, balloons would drift back to the ground when the air inside them cooled.

The two men had to stay awake for long periods of time to keep the balloon *(firm/firmly)* on its course around the world. When Piccard and Jones finally landed, they got a warm welcome and much-needed rest.

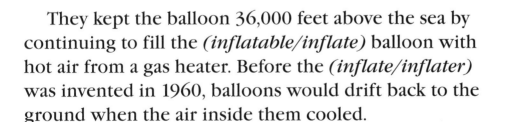

Vocabulary List

1. brittle
2. damp
3. misshapen
4. lean
5. fragile
6. submerge
7. firm
8. rumple
9. flexible
10. inflate

3 Build New Vocabulary

The Prefix *mis-*

 Write each word from the box below next to its correct definition. Use a dictionary if you need help.

misfit	misguide	misinform	misjudge
mislay	misshapen	misspent	misstate
mistreat	mistrust		

1. to behave badly to someone or something _____

2. to put something in a place that is later forgotten _____

3. to say the wrong thing _____

4. to not have faith in _____

5. spent in a bad or foolish way _____

6. someone or something that does not fit or belong in a group _____

7. to show the wrong way _____

8. to decide something unfairly _____

9. to give the wrong information _____

10. formed badly _____

Word Play

Riddles

 Answer each riddle below by writing the vocabulary word that best fits. The boldfaced word in each riddle contains some of the letters of the correct vocabulary word.

1. The captain does this to a **submarine** at the beginning of a journey.

   _____

2. If you can **flex** your arms and legs easily, you are this.

   _____

3. If you are **leaning** against a fence and people can hardly see you, you must be this.

   _____

4. If you put air **into** a balloon, you are doing this.

   _____

5. A very tall **fir** tree is this.

   _____

6. If you are **frail** and delicate, you are this.

   _____

7. The ground near a **dam** that is holding back water

   is this. _____

8. If you make a **mistake** when you are creating something, it will turn out like this.

   _____

Physical Conditions • Word Play   Score _____ (Top Score 8)   Unit 5 • Lesson 28   **113**

1. **column**
(kol´ əm) *n.*
a list of written items

2. **arrange**
(ə rānj´) *v.*
to put in order

3. **series**
(sir´ ēz) *n.*
events happening
one after another

4. **precede**
(pri sēd´) *v.*
to come before

5. **schedule**
(skej´ ōo əl) *n.*
a plan of things
to do

6. **ascend**
(ə send´) *v.*
to move upward;
rise

7. **descend**
(di send´) *v.*
to move downward

8. **disarray**
(dis´ ə rā´) *n.*
lack of order

9. **junior**
(jōōn´ yər) *adj.*
younger or
lower ranked

10. **senior**
(sēn´ yər) *adj.*
older or higher
ranked

"Order" Vocabulary

1 Word Meanings

Synonyms

 Write the vocabulary word that is a synonym for each boldfaced word or phrase.

1. **Older** people over 65 years old _____

2. The baseball season ends with a **set** of games one after another. _____

3. A bus **timetable** tells what time all of the buses come and go. _____

4. **Younger** high school students are usually in the seventh and eighth grades. _____

5. The numbers in an account should be written in a neat **list.** _____

6. Before school starts in the fall, most teachers **organize** their classrooms. _____

7. Hot-air balloons **rise** into the air. _____

8. Most parents don't like to see their children's rooms in a state of **disorder.** _____

9. To get on a subway train, one must **go down** under the ground. _____

10. The months of May and June **come before** the month of July. _____

② Reference Skills

Phonetic Spellings

 Pronounce each phonetic spelling below. Then choose the vocabulary word that is a synonym of each phonetic spelling and write it in the blank.

Phonetic Spelling   **Synonym**

1. rīz   _____

2. ōld′ ər   _____

3. tīm′ tābəl   _____

4. singk   _____

5. mes′ ē nes   _____

6. yung′ ger   _____

7. or′ dər   _____

8. list   _____

• •

Read each question below and pronounce each phonetic spelling. Then write *Yes* or *No* to answer each question.

9. Could a bird /ə send′/ ? _____

10. Could your calendar be your /skej′ o͞o əl/ ? _____

11. If something has no order, has it been /ə rānjd′/ ?

   _____

12. Does a baby /pri sēd′/ his or her mother? _____

13. If something has no order, is it in /dis′ ə rā′/ ?

   _____

14. Is a /kol′ əm/ a kind of dance? _____

Vocabulary List

1. column
2. arrange
3. series
4. precede
5. schedule
6. ascend
7. descend
8. disarray
9. junior
10. senior

3 Build New Vocabulary

The Prefix *dis-*

Read the sentences below. Write the word from the box that correctly completes each sentence. Use a dictionary if you need help.

discolored	discontinue	disagreeable	dishonest
dismount	disregard	disbelieve	displeased
disarray	disarrange		

1. If you _____ someone, you do not believe him.

2. A piece of cloth that is _____ has lost its color or faded.

3. A person who is _____ about something is unhappy about it.

4. A messy room is in a state of _____.

5. When someone is not telling the truth, the person is being _____.

6. To get off a horse or bicycle is to _____ from it.

7. If you _____ something, you do not regard, or pay any attention, to it.

8. To _____ something means to put an end to it.

9. To _____ something means to change or disturb the arrangement of it.

10. Someone who is _____ is not fun to be with because she will not agree with you.

Score _____ (Top Score 10) "Order" Vocabulary • Build New Vocabulary

 **Word Play**

Sentence Completion

Complete the passage below by writing the correct vocabulary word in each blank. (**Hint:** You will need to add *-ing* to one of the words.)

School Day Schedule

If you are not organized and your days are always in

_____, you might want to plan your

time by writing a _____.

You can _____, or order, your day on a piece of paper. Write the hours of the day in

a _____, or list.

Start writing at the bottom of the paper and move

up to the top of the paper in _____ order. Begin with the time you wake up and end with the time you go to bed.

Next write what you plan to do during each hour. Think about the order in which your

_____ of activities takes place.

If you practice making and using schedules, you will be able to plan your time well when you get to

middle school or _____ high school.

By the time you are a _____ student in high school and ready to graduate, you will be an expert at organizing your time!

Vocabulary Review

 Review Word Meanings

Read the passage below. Then answer the questions about the boldfaced vocabulary words.

Constructing an Office Building

When a company is growing and making large **profits,** the executives might decide that they need a new office building. There are **numerous** tasks that must be completed to construct an office building. First an **architect** draws a **series** of plans until he or she is satisfied with the way that everything in the building will be **arranged.** For a large project, a **senior** architect rather than a **junior** architect is usually given the job.

Now read the following questions. Then completely fill in the bubble of the correct answer.

1. Which of the following words means "organized" or "put in order"?
   Ⓐ arranged
   Ⓑ series
   Ⓒ senior

2. Which of the following is the definition of *architect* in the passage above?
   Ⓐ a person who constructs buildings
   Ⓑ a person who fixes buildings
   Ⓒ a person who designs and plans buildings

3. Which of the following is a synonym of *numerous* in the passage above?
   Ⓐ number
   Ⓑ many
   Ⓒ countless

4. Which of the following is a definition of *series?*
   Ⓐ a lack of order
   Ⓑ events following one after another
   Ⓒ the greatest amount possible

5. What is the relationship between *senior* and *junior* in the passage above?
   Ⓐ They have the same meaning.
   Ⓑ They have opposite meanings.
   Ⓒ They have unrelated meanings.

6. Which of the following is true, according to the passage above?
   Ⓐ When a company makes a lot of money, it might need a new building.
   Ⓑ When a company is losing money, it might need a new building.
   Ⓒ When a company makes machines, it will need a new building.

② Review Word Meanings

Read the passage below. Then answer the questions about the boldfaced vocabulary words.

Costs of Constructing an Office Building

A person called an accountant must figure out the **sum** of the costs that will be involved with building an office building. The accountant will list all of the costs of materials and **wages** for workers in a **column** in an **account.** The company that will own the building must be able to **afford** to build it. Otherwise the company will not be able to pay all the **bills** involved and might then go **bankrupt.**

Now read the following questions. Then completely fill in the bubble of the correct answer.

1. Which of the following is a correct definition of *wages* in the passage above?
   Ⓐ money that is spent
   Ⓑ money that is owed to another
   Ⓒ money that is paid for work or services

2. If a person can *afford* something, the person _____.
   Ⓐ is able to buy it
   Ⓑ is not able to buy it
   Ⓒ must borrow money to buy it

3. Which of the following statements is *not* true?
   Ⓐ A column of numbers is listed in an account.
   Ⓑ Wages can be used to pay bills.
   Ⓒ A person who pays all his or her bills is bankrupt.

4. Which of the following word pairs contains two types of written records?
   Ⓐ wages, sum
   Ⓑ account, bills
   Ⓒ wages, column

5. Which of the following is the mathematical operation that produces a *sum?*
   Ⓐ addition
   Ⓑ subtraction
   Ⓒ division

6. Which of the following is true, according to the passage above?
   Ⓐ An accountant pays the workers.
   Ⓑ An accountant makes a list of how much the workers are paid.
   Ⓒ An accountant affords the workers.

③ Review Word Meanings

Read the passage below. Then answer the questions about the boldfaced vocabulary words.

Following a Plan for Building

Once the plan of a building is complete and the **expenses** have been **tallied,** a **schedule** for actually constructing the building is prepared. A schedule prevents the construction of a building from falling into a state of **disarray.** It shows the **maximum** amount of time that it should take to construct the building. It also shows which steps **precede** other steps. Although it is important for the workers to stick to the schedule, it must be **flexible** to allow for problems that might come up.

Now read the following questions. Then completely fill in the bubble of the correct answer.

1. Which of the following words includes a prefix that means "not"?
   Ⓐ expenses
   Ⓑ disarray
   Ⓒ precede

2. Which of the following words means the opposite of *maximum?*
   Ⓐ most
   Ⓑ least
   Ⓒ many

3. Which of the following words means the same as *tallied?*
   Ⓐ paid
   Ⓑ completed
   Ⓒ counted

4. Which of the following is the definition of *precede* in the passage above?
   Ⓐ come before
   Ⓑ come after
   Ⓒ move upward

5. Which of the following word pairs contains synonyms of *flexible?*
   Ⓐ bendable, breakable
   Ⓑ bendable, changeable
   Ⓒ delicate, brittle

6. Which of the following is true, according to the passage above?
   Ⓐ A building schedule shows the money spent.
   Ⓑ A building schedule shows a disarray of steps.
   Ⓒ A building schedule shows which steps come before other steps.

4 Review Word Meanings

Read the passage below. Then answer the questions about the boldfaced vocabulary words.

Completing the Building

Once the foundation and frame of the building are in place, the building is **partially** finished. Then a **carpenter** begins to build the wooden structures inside the building. Many buildings have wood floors, doors, and cupboards because wood is a **firm** material. It is not **brittle** or **fragile,** and if it has been prepared correctly it does not become **misshapen** when it becomes **damp.**

Now read the following questions. Then completely fill in the bubble of the correct answer.

1. Which of the following is true, according to the passage above?
   - Ⓐ The building is finished once the frame is in place.
   - Ⓑ The building is halfway finished once the frame is in place.
   - Ⓒ The building is not yet begun once the frame is in place.

2. Which of the following is the correct definition of the prefix *mis-* in *misshapen?*
   - Ⓐ not or the opposite of
   - Ⓑ before
   - Ⓒ badly or wrongly

3. If something is *damp,* it is _____.
   - Ⓐ soaking wet
   - Ⓑ slightly wet
   - Ⓒ not wet

4. Which of the following is the definition of *fragile* in the passage above?
   - Ⓐ delicate and needing special care
   - Ⓑ easily bendable or changeable
   - Ⓒ badly formed

5. Which of the following word pairs means the opposite of *firm?*
   - Ⓐ strong, flexible
   - Ⓑ lean, brittle
   - Ⓒ weak, shaky

6. A carpenter builds wooden structures because _____.
   - Ⓐ that is his or her job
   - Ⓑ wood is fragile
   - Ⓒ the foundation is damp

1. **meadow**
   (med′ ō) *n.*
   piece of grassy land

2. **cultivate**
   (kul′ tə vāt′) *v.*
   to prepare land for planting

3. **graze**
   (grāz) *v.*
   to feed on grass

4. **furrow**
   (fûr′ ō) *n.*
   long rut made by a plow

5. **roam**
   (rōm) *v.*
   to wander

6. **maintain** bảo tồn
   (mān tān′) *v.* giữ gìn
   to care for ↓ sửi khvê

7. **bale**
   (bāl) *n.*
   large bundle tied tightly

8. **chute**
   (shoōt) *n.*
   a narrow, sloping passageway

9. **stall**
   (stôl) *n.*
   animal's room in a barn

10. **silo**
    (sī′ lō) *n.*
    a tall tower for storing grain

Country Life

(1) Word Meanings

Sentence Completion

Complete each sentence below by writing the correct vocabulary word in the blank.

1. It takes hard work for a farmer to

   _____ the land to prepare it for

   planting crops.

2. First the farmer uses a plow to make a

   _____ in the field.

3. When the _____ is full of grain,
   the farmer feels ready for winter.

4. During the day, the cows _____
   over the hills.

5. As they wander, the cows _____
   and feed on the grass.

6. In spring, the grass in the _____
   next to the creek grows very quickly.

7. After the hay is harvested, the farmer rolls it up into

   a large _____.

8. The floor of a horse's _____ is
   covered with fresh hay.

9. Farmers _____ their fields by
   plowing them both before and after the growing
   season.

10. Before the sheeps' wool is trimmed, the farmer herds

    them through a _____ and into
    a pen.

2 Reference Skills

Words with Multiple Meanings

 Read the following dictionary entries. Then read each sentence below. Write the number of the correct definition for the boldfaced word in each sentence.

---

bale *n.* **1.** a large bundle tied tight **2.** sadness

chute *n.* **1.** a narrow, sloping passageway **2.** a fast, shallow place in a river **3.** a steep slope in the snow

furrow *v.* **1.** to make furrows with a plow **2.** to make wrinkles on

graze *v.* **1.** to feed on grass **2.** to scrape the skin a little bit

---

1. Worrying about the lack of rain **furrowed** the farmer's face. _____

2. As soon as the fence was built, the farmer herded the cows into the field to **graze.** _____

3. Juan's heart beat fast as his sled swooshed down the snowy **chute.** _____

4. Some farmers still use horses to **furrow** their fields.

   _____

5. A ton of hay makes about 35 **bales.**

   _____

6. The sharp thorns on the bushes **grazed** her legs as she ran. _____

Vocabulary List

1. *meadow*

2. *cultivate*

3. *graze*

4. *furrow*

5. *roam*

6. *maintain*

7. *bale*

8. *chute*

9. *stall*

10. *silo*

3 Build New Vocabulary

The Suffixes *-or* and *-er*

Complete the passage below with the *-or* and *-er* words from the box.

---

cultivator: a machine that loosens soil and destroys weeds

baler: a machine that makes bales

rancher: one who owns a ranch

herder: one who makes a herd of animals move

harvester: a machine that harvests

shearer: one who cuts off sheep's wool

Country Life

Life in the country involves many different jobs. In

early spring a farmer must run a _____
between the furrows to break up the ground and keep
the weeds from growing.

Spring is also the time when a sheep

_____ hires a helper called a

_____ to cut the wool off the female
sheep before the lambs are born. After the lambs are
born, the sheep are all moved to the green meadows. An

extra _____ might be hired to help
drive the flock of sheep.

In the late summer the farmer runs a

_____ over the hay fields. The bales
are put into the barn to be stored for the winter. A farmer

also runs a _____ through the field to
gather the grain. Grain is stored in a silo for feeding later
in the winter.

Word Play
Metaphors

 Use the vocabulary words to complete the following metaphors.

1. A really interesting story will help you think new thoughts. A good book is a farmer who can

   _____ your mind and sow the seeds of imagination.

2. Their teacher was very wise. They knew her mind

   was a _____ filled with grains of information.

3. A brisk breeze whisked over the tops of the trees, over the rolling hills, over the soft, grassy fields. The

   _____ was an ocean with waves of grass rolling over it.

4. As much as she tried to listen, she kept thinking about other things. The girl's imagination was a wild

   horse that would _____ all over.

5. This room is an animal _____— although I think an animal would not want to live with all this dirt.

6. He didn't like to just eat lunch—he wanted to be a

   sheep that _____ on blades of grass all day.

"Geography" Vocabulary

Word Meanings

Definition Sentences

Complete each sentence below by writing the vocabulary word that the sentence defines.

Vocabulary List

1. **summit**
(sum´ it) *n.*
the highest part

2. **altitude**
(al´ ti tōōd´) *n.*
height above sea level

3. **ravine**
(rə vēn´) *n.*
deep, narrow valley carved by a river

4. **latitude**
(lat´ i tōōd´) *n.*
distance on Earth north or south

5. **longitude**
(lon´ ji tōōd´) *n.*
distance on Earth east or west

6. **equator**
(i kwā´ tər) *n.*
imaginary line around Earth's middle

7. **glacier**
(glā´ shər) *n.*
a slowly moving ice mass

8. **mesa**
(mā´ sə) *n.*
a flat-topped hill

9. **formation**
(for mā´ shən) *n.*
something made

10. **peninsula**
(pə nin´ sə lə) *n.*
land with water on three sides

bán
đảo

1. A _____ is a piece of land that is surrounded by water on three sides.

2. The imaginary line around Earth that is halfway between the north and south poles is called the _____.

3. The highest part of a mountain is its _____.

4. A distance on Earth's surface north or south of the equator is called _____.

5. _____ is a distance on Earth east or west of an imaginary line called the prime meridian.

6. The height of a mountain's distance above sea level is its _____.

7. A _____ is a flat-topped hill or mountain with steep sides.

8. Mountains, caves, mesas, and canyons are all natural _____ on Earth.

9. A _____ is a deep, rocky valley with a river running along the bottom.

10. A large, slow-moving mass of ice is called a _____.

② Reference Skills

Using an Electronic Encyclopedia

Read the following dictionary entry and the information from an electronic encyclopedia. Then circle *dictionary* or *electronic encyclopedia* to answer each question below.

Dictionary Entry

gla•cier (glā′ shər) *n.* a large mass of ice that moves slowly over land

Electronic Encyclopedia Information

• Clicking *glacier* in the encyclopedia search gives 30 articles about glaciers.

• Clicking on the article called *Glacier* gives six different sections to read about glaciers, including *Alpine Glaciers, Piedmont Glaciers,* and *Icecap Glaciers.*

• Clicking on the section *Alpine Glaciers* gives a movie clip of how a glacier forms.

1. Which would tell you that *glacier* is a noun?
   dictionary or *electronic encyclopedia*

2. Where would you find information about how a glacier is formed?
   dictionary or *electronic encyclopedia*

3. Where could you watch a movie clip about how a glacier is formed?
   dictionary or *electronic encyclopedia*

4. Which would list a short definition of *glacier?*
   dictionary or *electronic encyclopedia*

5. If you were writing a report about glaciers, which would you use?
   dictionary or *electronic encyclopedia*

Vocabulary List

1. summit
2. altitude
3. ravine
4. latitude
5. longitude
6. equator
7. glacier
8. mesa
9. formation
10. peninsula

3 Build New Vocabulary

Adjective Forms

The words in the box below are adjective forms of the vocabulary words. Complete each sentence with the correct adjective from the box.

---

longitudinal: relating to longitude

glacial: relating to or coming from a glacier

equatorial: relating to the ēquator

formative: able to form or grow

latitudinal: relating to latitude

peninsular: relating to a peninsula

---

1. The _____, or growth, stage of most glaciers happened thousands of years ago.

2. The lines on a globe that run from the north pole to the south pole are called _____ lines.

3. The equator is the _____ line that is labeled 0 degrees on a globe.

4. Florida is a _____ piece of land that is surrounded by the Atlantic Ocean and the Gulf of Mexico.

5. Because part of Brazil is located on the equator, it is called an _____ country.

6. Many _____ valleys were formed as huge masses of moving ice cut into the ground.

4 Word Play

Words Inside Words

 Circle each word that could be formed using letters from the vocabulary words below. For some vocabulary words, all the choices might be correct.

1. **summit**
   a. smith   **b.** sit   **c.** mat

2. **altitude**
   a. date   **b.** it   **c.** tea

3. **canyon**
   a. an   **b.** on   **c.** cat

4. **latitude**
   a. ate   **b.** sat   **c.** tail

• •

Write the vocabulary word that contains all the words in each group below *and* matches the clue given.

5. in, is, sin, pen (**Clue:** Three sides wet, one side dry)

   _____

6. or, tar, rot, rat, rate, tear, tea (**Clue:** If Earth were a person, I'd hold up Earth's pants.)

   _____

7. lace, rice, ice, rag (**Clue:** Slowly moving; icy cold)

   _____

8. sea, me, am, as, same (**Clue:** I'm a mountain with a

   flat top.) _____

Vocabulary List

1. **misleading**
   (mis lē´ ding) *adj.*
   causing a wrong idea

2. **disgrace**
   (dis grās´) *n.*
   loss of honor; shame

3. **misplace**
   (mis plās´) *v.*
   to put in a wrong place

4. **misgiving**
   (mis giv´ ing) *n.*
   a feeling of doubt

5. **premature**
   (prē mə chûr´) *adj.*
   coming before the right time

6. **precaution**
   (pri kô´ shən) *n.*
   care taken beforehand

7. **relapse**
   (rē´ laps) *n.*
   a slipping back to an earlier state

8. **reunion**
   (rē ūn´ yən) *n.*
   gathering of people after a long time

9. **uneasy**
   (un ē´ zē) *adj.*
   worried and uncomfortable

10. **unforeseen**
    (un for sēn´) *adj.*
    not known beforehand; not expected

"Prefix Mix" Vocabulary

 1 **Word Meanings**

Definitions and Base Words

 Write each vocabulary word next to its correct definition below. Then write the base word from the box below that matches each vocabulary word.

lapse	union	ease	see	give
caution	lead	place	grace	mature

1. before the right time _____

2. a feeling of doubt _____

3. not known or expected before it happens _____

4. to slip back again to an earlier stage _____

5. a loss of honor; shame _____

6. causing a wrong or mistaken idea _____

7. to lose or put in the wrong place _____

8. a gathering of people after a long time _____

9. worried _____

10. care taken beforehand _____

② Reference Skills

Alphabetizing

 Arrange each group of words below in alphabetical order.

1. misgovern, misguide, misgiving

   _____

2. unending, uneasy, uneducated

   _____

3. disgrace, dishonest, disfigure

   _____

4. reveal, return, reunion

   _____

5. precaution, predate, prearrange

   _____

• •

Complete each sentence below with the correct vocabulary word.

6. Even with special machines made to tell when an earthquake will happen, earthquakes are often

   _____ and come as a surprise.

7. My dogs seem old, but when I play catch with them

   they have a _____ and act like puppies.

8. Spanish explorers believed stories about cities made of gold hidden somewhere in North or South America, but these stories were

   _____ and false.

Vocabulary List

1. *misleading*
2. *disgrace*
3. *misplace*
4. *misgiving*
5. *premature*
6. *precaution*
7. *relapse*
8. *reunion*
9. *uneasy*
10. *unforeseen*

3 Build New Vocabulary

Context Clues: Base Word Families

Use your knowledge of the vocabulary words to identify the meaning of each underlined word in the sentences below. Circle each correct answer.

1. Babies who are born <u>prematurely</u> are often smaller than they should be and need special care. *Prematurely* means:
   a. something happening before it should
   b. something happening after it should
   c. something happening when it should

2. Many people become nervous and experience <u>uneasiness</u> when they have to give a speech in front of many people. *Uneasiness* means:
   a. a strange feeling
   b. an excited feeling
   c. an uncomfortable feeling

3. Wearing a helmet while riding a bike is a good <u>precautionary</u> habit that can help prevent injuries. *Precautionary* means:
   a. done carelessly
   b. done to prevent future trouble
   c. done to obey the law

4. Most weather conditions can be predicted by weather <u>forecasters</u>, but sometimes the path that a storm takes is <u>unforeseeable</u>. *Unforseeable* means:
   a. something that cannot be seen ahead of time
   b. something that can be seen ahead of time
   c. something that can be changed

5. When eating at a fancy restaurant, using bad table manners may be thought <u>disgraceful</u>. *Disgraceful* means:
   a. bringing honor upon someone
   b. bringing nervousness upon someone
   c. bringing shame upon someone

 **Word Play**

Synonyms

 Each word in the box below is a synonym of one of the vocabulary words and contains the same prefix. Write each synonym from the box next to the correct vocabulary word.

misguiding	reuniting	uncomfortable
unexpected	dishonor	regress

1. misleading _____

2. reunion _____

3. uneasy _____

4. unforeseen _____

5. disgrace _____

6. relapse _____

 Think About It

Earn two extra points by using the underlined synonyms in the poem below to guess the missing vocabulary word.

Oh where did I put it,
It's <u>lost</u>, it's no more!
Did somebody steal it?
But whatever for?
I know I just had it,
It was just <u>mislaid</u>.

But to _____ your nose
Is quite odd, I'm afraid.

1. **downtown**
(doun′ toun′) *n.*
the business center
of a city

2. **offspring**
(ôf′ spring) *n.*
the young of an
animal or plant

3. **headquarters**
(hed′ kwor tərz) *n.*
place where the
leaders are

4. **overcome**
(ō′vər′cəm) *v.*
to conquer

5. **somewhat**
(sum′ hwut) *adv.*
to some degree

6. **background**
(bak′ ground) *n.*
the farthest part in
a picture

7. **halfhearted**
(haf′ här′ tid) *adj.*
without much interest

8. **highlights**
(hī′ līts) *n.*
the most important
parts

9. **funny bone**
(fun′ ē bōn) *n.*
part of the elbow
that tingles when
bumped

10. **lifelike**
(līf′ lik) *adj.*
looking very real

Compound Words

1   **Word Meanings**

Examples

 Write each vocabulary word next to its matching example or examples below.

1. The most important events in a movie

   _____

2. Lambs, chicks, colts, cubs, calves, and human babies

   _____

3. A painting of a person that looks just like the person

   _____

4. The part of the elbow that causes a tickling feeling

   when it is bumped _____

5. A business center; a place for shopping

   _____

6. To get over a fear _____

7. The location of the leaders of an army; the main

   offices of a business _____

8. Watching a game but not caring which team wins

   _____

9. The sky in the back of a painting of mountains

   _____

10. A game that is a little bit fun _____

② Reference Skills
Spelling and Definitions

Each boldfaced compound word in the questions below is written incorrectly. Write each one correctly and then answer each question with *Yes* or *No*.

1. Is it somewhat painful to hit your **funny-bone**

   _____? _____

2. Is **half-hearted** _____ less than

   excited but more than bored? _____

3. Is **down town** _____ the

   opposite of countryside? _____

4. Is conquer another word for **over come**

   _____? _____

5. Does **life-like** _____ mean

   like life? _____

6. Is a **high light** _____ a light that

   is too high to reach? _____

7. Is the **back-ground** _____ of a

   painting the part that is farthest away? _____

8. Are **head-quarters** _____ coins

   with heads on both sides? _____

Compound Words • Reference Skills   Score _____ (Top Score 16)   Unit 6 • Lesson 34   **135**

Vocabulary List

1. *downtown*

2. *offspring*

3. *headquarters*

4. *overcome*

5. *somewhat*

6. *background*

7. *halfhearted*

8. *highlights*

9. *funny bone*

10. *lifelike*

3 Build New Vocabulary

Forming Compound Words

Use a word from the first box and a word from the second box to build compound words that fit the definitions below. The words in parentheses are clues that will help you choose the correct words.

Box One	Box Two
head, life, down, half, back, high, funny, some	bone, hearted, ground, quarters, lights, like, town, what

1. the place at the back of the elbow

   _____   _____
   (silly)   (skeleton)

2. the place where a leader lives

   _____
   (brain + money)

3. the part of a painting showing what lies behind things

   _____
   (not in front + floor)

4. something of special interest

   _____
   (above + lamps)

5. a city's center of business _____
                                (not up + city)

6. to some extent _____
                  (a few + a question)

7. not very excited _____
                    (part + caring)

8. very realistic _____
                  (living + similar to)

Score _____ (Top Score 8)   Compound Words • Build New Vocabulary

Word Play

Compound Word Meanings

Answer the question about each compound word below by writing *Yes* or *No*.

1. Is a *hotdog* a sweaty puppy? _____

2. Is a *funny bone* a skeleton that tells jokes?

   _____

3. Does a *halfhearted* person only partly care about

   what is going on? _____

4. If a river *overflows*, does that mean water flows over

   the riverbank? _____

5. If someone *overcomes*, does that mean she comes

   over to your house? _____

6. Is a *lifelike* painting a painting that looks like real

   life? _____

7. Is an *offspring* a spring that bounces off of things?

   ng tiến góc   sự bật lên, tung lên

   _____

8. Are *headquarters* money for your brain to spend?

   _____

9. Are *highlights* lamps that are hung from the ceiling?

   _____

10. Is someone who is *open-minded* a person who keeps

    his mind open to new ideas? _____

1. **cram**
   (kram) *v.*
   to pack tightly

2. **clutch**
   (kluch) *v.*
   to grasp or hold
   tightly

3. **eject**
   (i jekt') *v.*
   to force out or
   throw out

4. **hoist**
   (hoist) *v.*
   to pull up or raise

5. **droop**
   (dro͞op) *v.*
   to hang down
   weakly

6. **swipe**
   (swīp) *v.*
   to hit with a
   sweeping motion

7. **shatter**
   (shat' ər) *v.*
   to suddenly break
   into many pieces

8. **knead**
   (nēd) *v.*
   to mix by pressing
   and squeezing

9. **mold**
   (mōld) *v.*
   to form or shape
   something

10. **lunge**
    (lunj) *v.*
    to suddenly move
    forward

More Action Words

1 Word Meanings

Synonyms

 Write each vocabulary word next to its
synonyms below.

1. lift, raise, pull up _____

2. dive, leap, pounce _____

3. hit, stroke _____

4. drive out, throw out _____

5. break, smash, burst _____

6. seize, grasp, grab _____

7. blend, mix, squeeze _____

8. dangle, hang, wilt _____

9. form, shape, build _____

10. stuff, jam, pack _____

• •

 Complete each sentence below with the correct
vocabulary word. You will need to add *-ed* to the
end of each word.

11. The farm workers _____ the heavy bales
    of hay into the hayloft.

12. The cat sat perfectly still. Suddenly she

    _____ forward.

13. The glass fell and _____ into hundreds
    of pieces.

14. Everything was dry. The bean plants _____
    and hung limply.

② Reference Skills

Words with Multiple Meanings

 Read the following dictionary entries, sentences, and boldfaced words. Decide how each boldfaced word is being used and write the number of its definition in the blank.

---

clutch *v.* **1.** to grasp or hold tightly *n.* **2.** a pedal that allows a driver to shift gears **3.** the number of eggs in a nest **4.** a group of chickens

cram *v.* **1.** to force into a crowded space **2.** to study fast and for a long time

mold *v.* **1.** to form or shape something *n.* **2.** furry growth on food or other damp object

---

1. The **clutch** of hens wandered around the barnyard.

_____

2. Sasha noticed that there was **mold** growing on the

bread in the refrigerator. _____

3. It is not a good idea to **cram** for a test instead of

keeping up with one's daily studying. _____

4. Hamsters like to **cram** food into their cheeks.

_____

5. It is wise for a woman to **clutch** her purse close to

her side when walking in large crowds. _____

6. Jake likes to **mold** animal figures out of clay.

_____

Vocabulary List

1. cram
2. clutch
3. eject
4. hoist
5. droop
6. swipe
7. shatter
8. knead
9. mold
10. lunge

3 Build New Vocabulary

Context Clues: Cloze Sentences

 Write the vocabulary word that completes each sentence below.

1. Magpies are birds that build huge nests and

_____ them full of shiny things that they have found.

2. Mother managed to _____ just in time to keep the glass from falling to the floor and shattering.

3. When a flag is first put on a flagpole it may

_____, but after we

_____ it to the top of the flagpole, it waves in the breeze.

4. David will _____ the bread

dough, and then he will _____ it into a round ball.

5. Baby monkeys _____ their mothers so that they will not fall out of the trees.

6. If you go into most restaurants without shoes on

your feet, the manager will _____ you from the building.

7. When a grizzly bear fishes for salmon, it will

_____ the fish with its claws.

8. Gulls carry clamshells high in the air and drop them

so they will _____ on the rocks below.

4 Word Play

Rhymes

 Write the correct form of one of the vocabulary words in the blank to complete each rhyme below.

1. Open the freezer and behold!
   All of the ice cubes are starting to

   _____!

2. The kids and dogs and cats have scattered

   Maybe something fragile _____.

3. I'm hungry, I'm tired, I'm beginning to

   _____.

   I'm hungry enough to eat mystery soup.

4. When there's a spill,
   My mother will
   Grab a sponge

   And make a _____!

● ●

Write the vocabulary word that rhymes with each set of words below.

5. goop, group, hoop   _____

6. crutch, hutch, much   _____

7. grunge, plunge, sponge   _____

8. gripe, hype, pipe   _____

9. bead, deed, feed   _____

10. checked, collect, expect _____

Vocabulary Review

 Review Word Meanings

Read the passage below. Then answer the questions about the boldfaced vocabulary words.

Farming

The United States has many fertile farms between 30 and 45 degrees **latitude** north of the **equator.** Most farmers in this area start to **cultivate** their fields in early spring. They begin by making long **furrows** in the fields with a plow.

Before they plant seeds, farmers must take the **precaution** of paying attention to the weather. This is because a few weeks of warm spring weather can be **somewhat misleading.** The planting of seeds must not be **premature,** because seedlings will die if the warm temperatures have a **relapse** into cold winter weather.

Now read the following questions. Then completely fill in the bubble of the correct answer.

1. Which of the following words means "to prepare land for planting crops"?
   Ⓐ cultivate
   Ⓑ furrows
   Ⓒ precaution

2. Which of the following is the definition of *latitude?*
   Ⓐ an imaginary line around the middle of Earth
   Ⓑ a distance on Earth north or south of the equator
   Ⓒ a distance on Earth east or west of the prime meridian

3. Which of the following words means "something that gives a wrong idea"?
   Ⓐ precaution
   Ⓑ misleading
   Ⓒ relapse

4. Which of the following is a definition of *premature?*
   Ⓐ fully grown
   Ⓑ too late
   Ⓒ before the right time

5. Which of the following is a definition of *somewhat?*
   Ⓐ some of what is there
   Ⓑ to some degree
   Ⓒ what is sometimes true

② Review Word Meanings

Read the passage below. Then answer the questions about the boldfaced vocabulary words.

Farmers' Duties

Once the seeds have been planted, farmers **maintain** and preserve their fields by weeding them. If there is not enough rain and the plants begin to **droop,** farmers must **overcome** this problem by watering the plants. Many farmers also put **lifelike** scarecrows in their fields to scare away birds that want to eat the crops.

When it is time for the harvest, farmers gather the hay and tie it up into large **bales.** They pour the grain into a long **chute** leading to a **silo** where the grain will be stored. A large supply of grain prevents a farmer from feeling **uneasy** about not having enough food in case of **unforeseen** misfortunes.

Now read the following questions. Then completely fill in the bubble of the correct answer.

1. Which of the following compound words has the same meaning as *unexpected?*
   Ⓐ overcome
   Ⓑ lifelike
   Ⓒ unforeseen

2. If a person is *uneasy* about something, the person _____.
   Ⓐ thinks that it is too hard to do
   Ⓑ feels assured about it
   Ⓒ feels nervous and worried about it

3. Which of the following words from the passage above is a synonym of *maintain?*
   Ⓐ cultivate
   Ⓑ preserve
   Ⓒ prepare

4. Which of the following words means "a tall building used for storing grain"?
   Ⓐ bale
   Ⓑ chute
   Ⓒ silo

5. Which of the following is the definition of *overcome* in the passage above?
   Ⓐ to come over
   Ⓑ to think over
   Ⓒ to conquer

3 Review Word Meanings

Read the passage below. Then answer the questions about the boldfaced vocabulary words.

Young Horses

During the spring, the **offspring** of horses and many other animals are born. Soon after a baby horse, called a foal, is born, its mother **hoists** it up upon its feet. A foal's legs are long and wobbly, and it sometimes **lunges** and falls as it learns how to walk.

Mother horses usually are kept in their **stalls** with their foals for a few days. Then the mothers and their foals are allowed to leave the barn and **roam** in **meadows** that are surrounded by fences. There the animals **graze** on the tender spring grass.

Now read the following questions. Then completely fill in the bubble of the correct answer.

1. Which of the following is the definition of *hoist*s in the passage above?
   - Ⓐ helps
   - Ⓑ grabs and holds tightly
   - Ⓒ pulls up or raises

2. Which of the following is the definition of *roam* as it is used in the passage above?
   - Ⓐ to suddenly move forward
   - Ⓑ to wander around
   - Ⓒ to run

3. Which of the following is a definition of *lunges?*
   - Ⓐ stops to look around
   - Ⓑ holds on tightly
   - Ⓒ moves suddenly forward

4. Which of the following groups of words includes only examples of *offspring?*
   - Ⓐ cows, horses, silos
   - Ⓑ stalls, foals, meadows
   - Ⓒ foals, puppies, kittens

5. Which of the following is a definition of *meadows?*
   - Ⓐ grassy areas of land
   - Ⓑ fields in which crops are planted
   - Ⓒ areas of land set aside for animals

6. Which of the following is true according to the passage above?
   - Ⓐ Mother and baby horses stay inside the house.
   - Ⓑ Mother and baby horses stay inside a room in the barn.
   - Ⓒ Mother and baby horses stay inside the hayloft.

4 Review Word Meanings

Read the passage below. Then answer the questions about the boldfaced vocabulary words.

A Reunion Treat

One **highlight** for many families who live in the country is a family **reunion.** To prepare for the guests, a farmer's wife might make fresh bread.

First she must mix flour, water, and eggs together into dough. Then she **kneads** the dough by **clutching** it firmly and moving it around with her hands. She **molds** the dough into a round **formation** and lets it rise. If she lives at a high **altitude,** she will have to watch the bread carefully because it will bake faster. Finally she puts it in the oven to bake.

....

Now read the following questions. Then completely fill in the bubble of the correct answer.

1. Which of the following is the definition of *highlight* in the passage above?
   Ⓐ a light that is attached to the top of a tall post
   Ⓑ the most important or most interesting part
   Ⓒ the last part

2. If a person is *clutching* something, the person is _____.
   Ⓐ getting it ready
   Ⓑ mixing it with his or her hands
   Ⓒ holding it tightly

3. Which of the following is a definition for *altitude?*
   Ⓐ height above a mountain
   Ⓑ height below sea level
   Ⓒ height above sea level

4. Which of the following is a definition of *reunion?*
   Ⓐ a weekly family dinner
   Ⓑ a gathering of people who have been apart for a long time
   Ⓒ a party that is held every year to celebrate the gathering of crops

5. Which of the following is a synonym of *molds?*
   Ⓐ forms
   Ⓑ bends
   Ⓒ crams

6. Which word below means "a person who mixes dough by squeezing and pushing it"?
   Ⓐ highlighter
   Ⓑ kneader
   Ⓒ molder

Cumulative Review

Definitions

Write the letter of the definition that matches each vocabulary word. (**Hint:** The words may appear in any lesson throughout the book.)

1. ____ open-minded

2. ____ pioneer

3. ____ veterinarian

4. ____ algae

5. ____ shingles

6. ____ faithfully

7. ____ precede

8. ____ ravine

9. ____ intelligence

10. ____ cobblestoned

11. _N_ cabinet

12. ____ headquarters

13. ____ lunge

14. ____ suggestion

15. _E_ annual

A. a deep, narrow valley worn by running water

B. simple water plants

C. open to new ideas

D. an idea that is offered

E. something that happens every year

F. to come before

G. first person to explore

H. paved with small, rounded stones

I. thin strips of wood on a roof

J. to move forward quickly

K. an animal doctor

L. the ability to learn, think, and understand

M. loyally and devotedly

N. a group that advises

O. place where the leaders are

Score _____ (Top Score 15)

Word Meanings

Antonyms

Write the letter of the antonym that matches each vocabulary word below. (**Hint:** Each vocabulary word is used once.)

1. _____ object   **A.** expert

2. _____ brittle   **B.** straight

3. _____ amateur   **C.** friendly

4. _____ gallant   **D.** strong

5. _____ crooked   **E.** agree

6. __H__ release   **F.** fresh

7. _____ uneasy   **G.** calm

8. __K__ maximum   **H.** capture

9. _____ deliberately   **I.** cowardly

10. _____ attractive   **J.** find

11. __L__ junior   **K.** minimum

12. _____ humble *hen mon*   **L.** senior
              bai lon

13. _____ hostile   **M.** accidentally

14. _____ stale   **N.** ugly

15. _____ misplace   **O.** proud

Score _____ (Top Score 15)   **Cumulative Review** **147**

Sentence Completion

 Write the vocabulary word that best completes each sentence below. Each sentence contains a clue related to a lesson theme. (**Hint:** The vocabulary words may appear in any lesson throughout the book.)

1. It is _____ and sad when there is conflict between two friends.

2. Hitting his _____ made him cry out in pain.

3. When an _____ moves to another country, she may not know anyone.

4. A bicycle pump is used to _____ a tire and change its physical condition.

5. A _____ is a person who goes on an exploration for gold and riches.

6. New Year's _____ is a time when people celebrate the end of the year.

7. He took action, grabbed a sponge, and used it to

   _____ all of the water on the table.

8. A _____ is the wooden skeleton that supports a house.

9. A _____ environment is one that is hot and near the equator.

10. A _____ helps people and speaks for them in court.

Words and Themes

 Choose two words from the box that belong with each theme below. Write the words in the blank. Try to complete the exercise without looking at the Vocabulary List in each lesson.

1. "Money" Vocabulary _____

2. "Friendship" Vocabulary _____

3. Storytelling Vocabulary _____

4. City Wildlife _____

5. Country Life _____

6. "Imagination" Vocabulary _____

conclusion
invisible
expense
preserve
wages
fable
companion
invent
silo
regard
mammals
furrow

Word Maps

Word maps help you think about how words connect to each other. They can help you learn and remember the meanings of words.

The word maps below are for vocabulary words in this book.

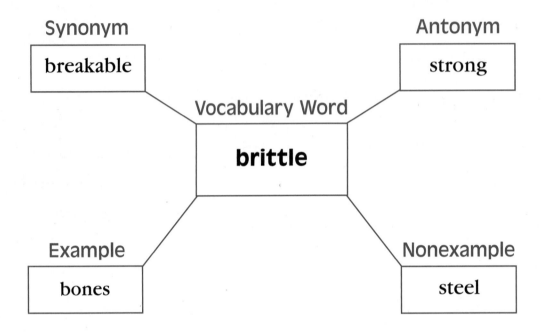

Synonym
breakable

Antonym
strong

Vocabulary Word
brittle

Example
bones

Nonexample
steel

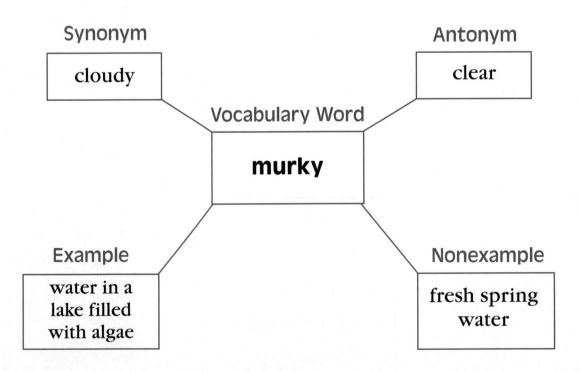

Synonym
cloudy

Antonym
clear

Vocabulary Word
murky

Example
water in a lake filled with algae

Nonexample
fresh spring water

Categorization

You can put words into groups or categories. This can help you learn the meanings of new words.

Look at this list of words:

colony	amateur
architect	headquarters
prospector	immigrant
chapel	pioneer
frontier	tavern

You can place these words into groups to help you remember their meanings.

People

pioneer

immigrant

architect

amateur

prospector

Places

colony

chapel

headquarters

frontier

tavern

Categorizing can help you learn new words in any subject. This is how you might categorize some of the words shown above if you were studying American history:

Words Related to Early America

colony

pioneer

frontier

prospector

immigrant

Linear Graphs

Linear graphs show words in different kinds of order. Drawing a linear graph can help you learn new words and how they relate to words you already know.

The linear graph below shows time order.

New Word

The words in the graph below show degrees of feeling.

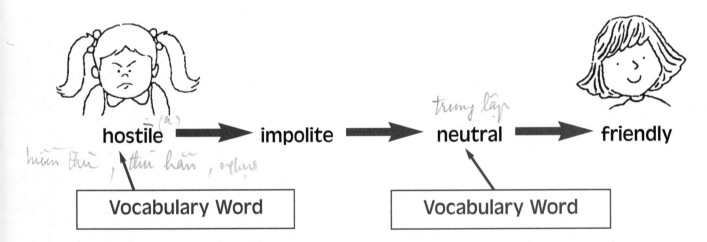

Vocabulary Word

Vocabulary Word

Another type of linear graph starts with a general word and gets more specific.

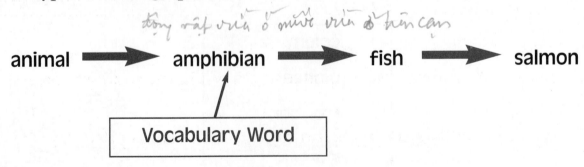

Vocabulary Word

Context Clues

You can learn about the meaning of a word from the other words around it. This is called using **context clues**. Remember that sometimes there are no context clues. The following are different kinds of context clues you can look for when you read:

Definition Clues

Sometimes the definition of a word is in the sentence.

My friend is <u>thoughtful</u>, which means she cares about the well-being of other people.

The word *thoughtful* means "caring about other people."

Example Clues

Sometimes examples in the sentence show the meaning of a word.

People drive <u>vehicles</u> such as cars and trucks.

Cars and trucks are examples of *vehicles*. A *vehicle* is a device used to transport people or things.

Comparison Clues

Sometimes a word means the same thing as a word in the sentence or a nearby sentence.

Sara was <u>exhausted</u>. Her friends were very tired, too.

Exhausted means "very tired."

Contrast Clues

Sometimes a word means the opposite of a word in the sentence or a nearby sentence.

Maria is really <u>serious</u>, even though she seems silly.

The word *serious* means the opposite of *silly*.

Context Clues

You can use context clues when you read. They help you learn more words.

NEW WORD

Antonio had finally reached the mountain's <u>summit</u>. As he stood at the <u>top of the mountain</u>, he could see faraway hills and fields. He slept there that night, but in the morning he began the <u>climb down</u>.

CONTEXT CLUE

CONTEXT CLUE

Summit means "the highest part of a mountain."

....

How to Use Context Clues

1. Look at the sentence.
2. Point to the word or words you do not know.
3. Ask yourself, "Is the meaning of the word in the sentence?"
4. Ask yourself, "Is the opposite meaning of the word in the sentence?"
5. Look at the sentences before and after the word or words you do not know to find more clues.

Word Relationships

Synonyms

A **synonym** is a word that has the same, or almost the same, meaning as another word.

Large and *big* are synonyms, so the following sentences mean the same thing:

That elephant is *large*.   That elephant is *big*.

Synonyms
small—tiny
start—begin
adorable—cute
gallant—brave
loyal—faithful

Antonyms

An **antonym** is a word or phrase that means the opposite of another word.

Light and *heavy* are antonyms because *light* means something that does not weigh very much and *heavy* means something that weighs a lot. *Rough* and *smooth* are also antonyms.

Antonyms
happy—sad
tall—short
grubby—clean
crooked—straight
humble—proud

Word Relationships
Homophones

Homophones are words that sound the same but have different meanings and spellings. *Waste* and *waist* sound the same, but *waste* means "objects that are left over or thrown away" and *waist* means "the middle part of your body."

What do you call a cold pepper? (a chilly chili)

Homographs

Homographs are words that are spelled the same but have different meanings. *Rest* can mean "to sleep," but *rest* can also mean "what is left."

After Ann ate the *rest,* she had to *rest.*

Some words that are spelled the same do not sound the same. You have *tears* when you cry, but when a book rips, it *tears.*

What do you call a boring field? (A plain plain)

Base Word Families

Base word families are groups of words that all share the same base word. Words in a base word family often have meanings that are related.

All the words below are built around the base word *lead.*

> **leadership:** the ability to lead or guide others
>
> **misleading:** describes something that leads you in the wrong direction
>
> **leader:** a person who gives directions

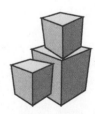

Building Vocabulary Skills

Notebook Reference

To Reinforce Vocabulary Skills

Tools and Reference

Table of Contents

www.sra4kids.com

Send all inquiries to:
SRA/McGraw-Hill
8787 Orion Place
Columbus, OH 43240-4027

Printed in the United States of America.

R00004411

1 2 3 4 5 6 7 8 9 QPD 07 06 05 04 03 02

Columbus, OH • Chicago, IL • Redmond, WA

The **McGraw·Hill** Companies

The History of Words

The English language gets words from interesting places.

Some words come from people's names.

> **sandwich**   This word comes from a story about man called the Earl of Sandwich. One evening he wanted a quick dinner, so he asked for meat between two pieces of bread. Soon his friends started asking for "sandwiches," too. Many people believe that the word *sandwich* came from his name.

Some words are borrowed from other languages.

> **mesa**   This word comes from the Spanish word that means "table." *Mesa* in English means "a flat-topped hill," which is a hill that looks like a table.

Some words are made up to describe something new.

> **basketball**   Basketball was invented by a man named Dr. James Naismith at a college in Massachusetts in 1891. The first basketball hoops were peach baskets with their bottoms cut out, so Dr. Naismith called his game *basketball.*

Prefixes and Suffixes
Prefixes

Prefixes can be added to the beginnings of base words to make new words.

Prefix	Meaning
bi-	two of something
de-	to do the opposite of; to remove
dis-	not
in-, im-	not
mis-	wrong
non-	not
over-	too much
pre-	before
re-	again
un-	not

You can add the prefix *un-* to the word *pleasant* to make the word *unpleasant,* or "not pleasant." You can add the prefix *re-* to the word *do* to make the word *redo,* or "to do again."

Suffixes

Suffixes can be added to the end of base words to make new words.

Suffix	Meaning
-able, -ible	is; can be
-er, -or	one who does something
-ful	full of
-less	without
-ness	have the quality of
-ous	full of
-y	being; having

You can add the suffix *-er* to the word *teach* to make the word *teacher,* or "one who teaches." You can add the suffix *-ous* to the word *joy* to make the word *joyous,* or "full of joy."

Base Words

A **base word** is a word with no prefixes or suffixes. It is the basic part of a word that carries the word's meaning.

Some Base Words

direct: to tell other people what to do

think: to have in your mind

visible: something you can see

array: an orderly grouping or arrangement

You can add prefixes and suffixes to base words to make **different words.**

Base Words With Prefixes and Suffixes Added

direct + or = director: a person who tells other people what to do

over + think = overthink: to think about something too much

in + visible = invisible: something you cannot see

dis + array = disarray: a lack of orderly arrangement

Noticing a base word inside of another word can sometimes help you figure out a word's meaning. For example, if you saw the word *misshapen,* you could figure out that the base word is *shape.* The word *shape* means "to make something or give a shape to something." The prefix *mis-* means "wrong." The word *misshapen* describes something that was badly or wrongly made.

German and Dutch Words

The English language has borrowed many words from other languages.
The words below may be spelled differently in their original forms.

Words Borrowed From German

ecology	science that studies living things and the places they live
delicatessen	a store where food that is ready to eat is sold
frankfurter	sausage
hamburger	a sandwich made with a patty of ground beef
loaf	shaped bread
polka	an upbeat German dance
pumpernickel	a dark bread made from rye flour
sauerkraut	cabbage that has been cut up and preserved in salt water
wild	living in nature

Words Borrowed From Dutch

bush	a small shrub
cookie	a small, flat cake
drill	to make a hole in something
luck	good fortune or happy chance
pickle	sour food that has been cooked in vinegar
sketch	a rough drawing
sled	a vehicle used to slide down a snowy or icy hill
split	to divide
stoop	to lean over
stove	a machine that burns fuel to cook food
wagon	a large cart
yacht	a sailboat or motorboat

Figurative Language

Words are fun. There are many ways to use words.

Sound Words

Sound words are words that sound like what they mean.

buzz	smash
clap	stomp
ring	squish
purr	slap
whoosh	beep

Similes

A **simile** uses *like* or *as* to compare one thing to another thing. You can say cold skin feels like ice. You can say a cat's fur is soft like a blanket.

Expressions

Sometimes words say one thing and mean another. A *stick in the mud* is not a real stick that is stuck in the mud. A *stick in the mud* is a person who will not try new things. If you say, "It is raining cats and dogs," it means it is raining very hard.

Some Expressions

green with envy: jealous

if the shoe fits, wear it: if there is a lesson for you, learn it

keep an eye out: watch for something

on a roll: having good luck

pulling your leg: teasing you; joking

Reference Skills
Using a Dictionary

Alphabetical Order

You can find a word in a dictionary by first looking at the beginning letter of the word. What if you wanted to find the word *clever* in a dictionary?

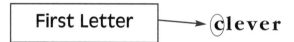

You would look in the part of the dictionary with words that begin with *c*. Once you find the *c* words, you need to look at the second letter of the word.

The second letter of *clever* tells you that *clever* is near the middle of the list of *c* words because *l* is in the middle of the alphabet. Sometimes you must look at the third or fourth letters of a word to find it on a dictionary page.

Reading a Dictionary Entry

If you look for the word *clever* in a dictionary, you might see this:

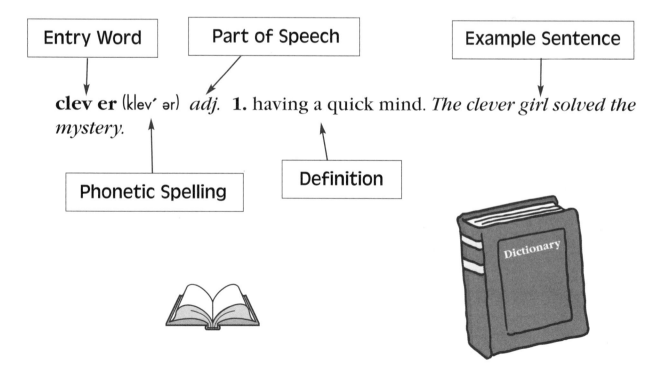

Reference Skills

Using a Thesaurus

A **thesaurus** shows synonyms, and sometimes antonyms, of a word.

If you looked up the word *extraordinary* in a thesaurus, you might see this:

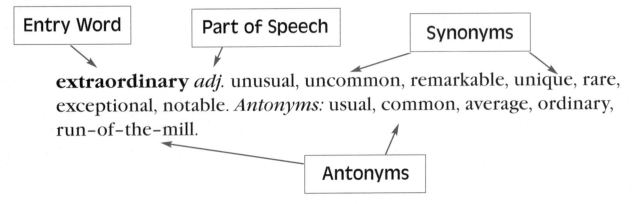

| Entry Word | Part of Speech | Synonyms |

extraordinary *adj.* unusual, uncommon, remarkable, unique, rare, exceptional, notable. *Antonyms:* usual, common, average, ordinary, run-of-the-mill.

| Antonyms |

Using an Encyclopedia

An **encyclopedia** is a set of books that has information about many topics. An encyclopedia can tell you a lot about words or topics. It will give you more information than a dictionary.

An encyclopedia set has many numbered books with topics or words in alphabetical order. You can also use an **electronic encyclopedia** on a computer.

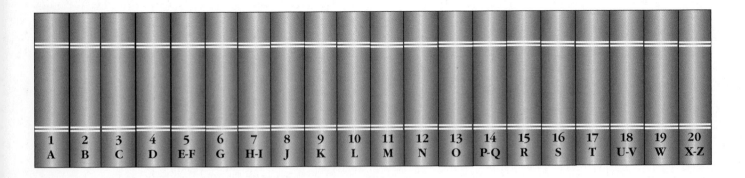

1 A	2 B	3 C	4 D	5 E-F	6 G	7 H-I	8 J	9 K	10 L	11 M	12 N	13 O	14 P-Q	15 R	16 S	17 T	18 U-V	19 W	20 X-Z

Parts of Speech

Nouns

Nouns name everything. Nouns are people, animals, places, things, or ideas. *Boy* is a noun because it names a person. *Cat* is a noun because it names an animal. *Truck* is a noun because it names a thing. *Freedom* is a noun because it is an idea.

Verbs

Verbs are action words. *Speak* is a verb because it is an action. *Lunge* is a verb because it is an action. Verbs are also state-of-being words. *Is* and *are* are verbs.

Adjectives

Adjectives are describing words. They tell about nouns. The word *anxious* is an adjective because it can describe *person*. *Dense* is an adjective because it can describe *fog*.

Adverbs

Adverbs are another kind of describing word. They usually describe verbs, but they can sometimes describe adjectives or other adverbs. *Willingly* is an adverb. You can *leave willingly. Promptly* is an adverb. You can *arrive promptly.*

Pronouns

Pronouns are words that can take the place of a noun, so you do not have to say a noun over and over. For example, *he* is a pronoun in this sentence: *Paul hurt his foot, so* he *had to go to the doctor.* Some other pronouns are *her, him, they,* and *it.*

Glossary

A

ab sorb /ab sorb´/ *v.* **absorbs, absorbing, absorbed. 1.** to soak up. *Use a paper towel to absorb the water on the table.* **2.** to take up the attention of. *My father was absorbed by the morning newspaper.*

ac count /ə kount´/ *n.* **1.** a written record of money spent or received. *My sister keeps the accounts for our family.* **2.** a sum of money held by a bank for a person or business. *Starting a savings account for college is a good idea.*

ac quire /ə kwīr´/ *v.* **acquires, acquiring, acquired.** to gain or get. *We acquired two hamsters and one bird last year.*

a dor a ble /ə dor´ə bəl/ *adj.* delightful; lovable; charming. *The little puppy was adorable.*

af ford /ə ford´/ *v.* **affords, afforded.** to be able to buy something. *We can afford a new car in two years.*

af ter ward /af´ tər wərd/ *adv.* at a later time. *We played tennis all afternoon and drank lemonade afterward.*

al gae /al´ jē/ *pl. n., sing.* **alga.** simple water plants. *Algae are water plants without stems or flowers.*

al ti tude /al ti tūd´/ *n.* the height that something is above sea level or the ground. *The plane was flying at an altitude of 25,000 feet.*

am a teur /am´ ə chər/ *n.* **1.** a beginner; not an expert. *He played a simple song on the piano because he was an amateur.* **2.** a person who does something for pleasure and not for pay. *My uncle is not a paid actor, but he is a talented amateur.*

am phib i ans /am fib´ ē ənz/ *pl. n.* **1.** egg-laying animals that live near water. *Amphibians do not have scales on their skin like snakes do.*

a mus ing /ə mūz´ ing/ *adj.* pleasing and entertaining. *My friend has an amusing way of telling a joke.*

an nu al /an´ ū əl/ *adj.* happening or returning once a year. *Graduation is an annual event at our school.*

arch /ärch/ *n., pl.* **arches.** a curved doorway over an open space. *Arches add grace and interest to many buildings.* *v.* to curve or form into an arch. *The cat arched its back and ran away.*

ar chi tect /är´ ki tekt´/ *n.* a person who designs buildings. *The architect brought us the plans for our new horse barn.*

arc tic /ärk´ tik/ *adj.* near the north pole; very cold. *Nearly all of the Arctic Ocean is covered with ice.*

ar range /ə rānj´/ *v.* **arranges, arranging, arranged.** to put in order. *Words in a dictionary are arranged in alphabetical order.*

as cend /ə send´/ *v.* **ascends, ascending, ascended.** to move upward; to rise. *The climbers ascended to the top of the mountain.*

as sem ble /ə sem′ bəl/ *v.* **assembles, assembling, assembled. 1.** to gather together. *Members of our neighborhood assemble once a month to discuss matters of interest.* **2.** to put together. *My parents assembled a model ship for my brother.*

as sist /ə sist′/ *v.* **assists, assisting, assisted.** to help; to give aid to. *I assisted my neighbor by walking his dog while he packed boxes for his move.*

as so ci ate /ə sō′ shē āt/ *v.* **associates, associating, associated. 1.** to join with or be friendly with. *Dogs and cats usually don't associate with one another.* **2.** to connect with in your mind. *Many people associate red roses with love.*

at trac tive /ə trak′ tiv/ *adj.* good-looking; pleasing. *A smile can make someone more attractive.*

au thor /ô′ thər/ *n.* a writer of stories, poems, articles, or other works of literature. *Margaret Mitchell was the author of only one book.*

B

back ground /bak′ ground/ *n.* **1.** the farthest part in a picture. *The part of a picture that seems to be in the distance is the background.* **2.** a person's learning or experience. *My friend's background is in chemistry.*

bag gy /bag′ ē/ *adj.* hanging loosely. *Baggy pants always sag.*

bale /bāl/ *n.* a large bundle tied tightly together. *The bales of hay were stacked in the meadow.*

bank rupt /bangk′ rupt/ *adj.* unable to pay debts. *Too many debts and not enough profits forced the bankrupt company to close its doors.*

bill /bil/ *n.* a written record or statement of money due. *Our heating bills are higher in the winter months.* *v.* **billing, billed.** to send a written notice of money owed to someone. *The repair person billed us the week after he fixed our oven.*

blue print /blū′ print′/ *n.* a drawn plan for a building. *Architects draw blueprints on special paper printed with white lines on a blue background.*

bon y /bō′ nē/ *adj.* very thin. *The stray dog looked bony and hungry.*

brit tle /brit′ əl/ *adj.* stiff and easily broken. *We broke up the brittle twigs of the tree for our campfire.*

bus tling /bus′ ling/ *adj.* a form of **bustle.** to move quickly and excitedly. *The bustling crowds on the sidewalks hurried to make their holiday purchases.*

/a/	at
/ā/	late
/â/	care
/ä/	father
/e/	set
/ē/	me
/i/	it
/ī/	kite
/o/	ox
/ō/	rose
/ô/	brought
	raw
/oi/	coin
/o͝o/	book
/o͞o/	too
/or/	form
/ou/	out
/u/	up
/yo͞o/	cube
/ûr/	turn
	germ
	learn
	firm
	work
/ə/	about
	chicken
	pencil
	cannon
	circus
/ch/	chair
/hw/	which
/ng/	ring
/sh/	shop
/th/	thin
/ŧh/	there
/zh/	treasure

C

cab i net /kab´ ə nit/ *n.* **1.** a group that advises a leader. *The cabinet supported the president's decision.* **2.** a piece of furniture with drawers, shelves, or doors. *My mother has assembled a large collection of plates and glasses in our china cabinet.*

can di date /kan´ di dāt´/ *n.* a person trying to get elected. *The governor has decided not to be a presidential candidate next year.*

cap ture /kap´ chər/ *v.* **captures, capturing, captured. 1.** to take by force. *The wolves were captured and moved to a safer environment.* **2.** to attract and hold. *The book's long title captured my interest. n.* the act of catching and holding someone or something. *The capture of the bear by zookeepers was a relief to the neighborhood.*

car pent er /kär´ pən tər/ *n.* a builder of wooden things. *A carpenter builds wooden cabinets and furniture.*

chap el /chap´ əl/ *n.* a little church. *There was a wedding in the chapel on Saturday morning.*

chute /shoot/ *n.* a narrow, sloping passageway. *Sheets and towels at the hotel are put down the laundry chute to the basement.*

clev er /klev´ ər/ *adj.* having an alert and quick mind. *Scientists are often very clever inventors.*

clutch /kluch/ *v.* **clutches, clutching, clutched.** to grasp or hold tightly. *My baby sister clutches my finger. n.* **1.** a pedal that allows a driver to shift gears. *The driver pushed the clutch down in order to start the car.* **2.** the number of eggs in a nest. *The chicken sat on her clutch of eggs.* **3.** a group of chickens. *The clutch of hens slept in the barn.*

cob ble stoned /kob´ əl stōnd/ *adj.* paved with a small, naturally round stone. *We walked unevenly over the cobblestoned streets.*

col lec tive /kə lek´ tiv/ *adj.* relating to a group; common; united. *A collective effort helped the team win. n.* a cooperative business or other undertaking. *The members of the grocery collective voted to reduce prices.*

colo nel /kûr´ nəl/ *n.* a leader of soldiers. *A colonel is an officer in the United States Army, Navy, or Marines.*

col o ny /kol´ ə nē/ *n., pl.* **colonies.** a land ruled by another country. *Thirteen British colonies became the first states of the United States.*

col umn /kol´ əm/ *n.* **1.** a list of written items. *The stories in a newspaper are arranged in columns.* **2.** an upright structure such as a post or pillar. *Tall columns on porches were used on many houses in the American South.*

com e dy /kom´ i dē/ *n., pl.* **comedies.** a funny play or story. *Many movies and television shows are comedies.*

com mis sion /kə mish ´ ən/ *n.*
1. a group gathered for special duties. *The mayor established a commission to study the city's water.*
2. money for services or work done. *Salesmen often receive a commission for every sale they make.* **3.** a position of rank in the military. *My brother will receive his commission as captain later this year. v.* **commissions, commissioned.** to give someone the right or power to do something. *The city commissioned a young artist to design the park.*

com mon ly /kom´ ən lē/ *adv.* usually; not rare. *Evergreen trees commonly grow in cool forests.*

com pan ion /kəm pan´ yən/ *n.*
1. a friend. *My dog is my companion.* **2.** something associated with a similar object. *The companion to this mitten is missing.*

com pass /kum´ pəs/ *n., pl.* **compasses.** a tool that shows directions. *A compass has a magnetic needle that points to the north. v.* **compasses, compassing, compassed.** to go around. *Their trip compassed the world.*

com plain /kəm plān´/ *v.* **complains, complaining, complained.** to talk about faults. *We complained to our teacher about the broken swings.*

con ceal /kən sēl´/ *v.* **conceals, concealing, concealed.** to hide or keep out of sight; to cover. *We concealed the key under the doormat.*

con cen tra tion /kon sən trā´ shən/ *n.* close attention. *My math homework requires all my concentration.*

con clu sion /kən kloo´ zhən/ *n.* the end or final part of something. *The exciting conclusion of the movie had all of us on the edge of our seats.*

con crete /kon ´ krēt/ *n.* a cement mixture. *Concrete can be made by mixing cement, pebbles, or sand with water.*

con fide /kən fīd´/ *v.* **confides, confiding, confided.** to tell as a secret. *I can always confide in my mother.*

con quer /kong´ kər/ *v.* **conquers, conquering, conquered. 1.** to take over by force. *The enemy army was conquered after a long war.* **2.** to overcome by effort. *He finally conquered his fear of flying.*

con scious /kon´ shəs/ *adj.* awake and aware. *After the accident, it was two hours before I was fully conscious.*

con sent /kən sent ´/ *v.* **consents, consenting, consented.** to say yes; to agree to. *The president did not consent to the senator's request.*

/a/	at
/ā/	late
/â/	care
/ä/	father
/e/	set
/ē/	me
/i/	it
/ī/	kite
/o/	ox
/ō/	rose
/ô/	brought
	raw
/oi/	coin
/o͝o/	book
/o͞o/	too
/or/	form
/ou/	out
/u/	up
/yo͞o/	cube
/ûr/	turn
	germ
	learn
	firm
	work
/ə/	about
	chicken
	pencil
	cannon
	circus
/ch/	chair
/hw/	which
/ng/	ring
/sh/	shop
/th/	thin
/ᵵℏ/	there
/zh/	treasure

con ser va tion /kon′ sər vā′ shən/ *n.* the protection of nature; preserving or protecting from loss or waste. *Conservation of Earth's natural resources is a concern for every person.*

con sid er /kən sid′ ər/ *v.* **considers, considering, considered.** to carefully think about before deciding. *My sister is considering whether or not to study in Europe next summer.*

con tri bu tion /kon′ trə bū′ shən/ *n.* something given. *Our family makes a yearly contribution to two charity services. The teacher said that my report made an important contribution to the class science fair.*

con trol /kən trōl′/ *n.* power over others. *The king had complete control of the country.* *v.* **controls, controlling, controlled.** to have power over; to command others. *I controlled the garden hose by holding it with both hands.*

co op er ate /kō op′ ə rāt/ *v.* **cooperates, cooperating, cooperated.** to work well with others. *We cooperated with another school on a recycling project.*

cram /kram/ *v.* **crams, cramming, crammed. 1.** to pack tightly or force into a crowded space. *Two more people crammed themselves into the crowded elevator.* **2.** to study fast. *She was cramming for the test.*

cre ate /krē āt′/ *v.* **creates, creating, created.** to make; to cause something to exist or to happen. *This director has created many amazing movies about the future.*

crook ed /krŏŏk′ id/ *adj.* bent or curving. *A crooked road leads down to the beach.*

cul ti vate /kul′ tə vāt/ *v.* **cultivates, cultivating, cultivated.** to prepare land for planting and growing flowers, vegetables, or other crops. *To cultivate land is to clear it and fertilize it before seeds are planted.*

cus tom ary /kus′ tə mer′ ē/ *adj.* usual. *It is customary to tip the waiter in a restaurant.*

D

damp /damp/ *adj.* a little bit wet. *Use a damp sponge to wipe the kitchen table.*

de bate /di bāt′/ *n.* a discussion about different opinions. *Our class held a debate to decide what the spring project would be.* *v.* **debates, debating, debated.** to discuss; to think about. *We debated for one hour. They debated whether to have a picnic that day.*

de ci sion /di sizh′ ən/ *n.* a judgment made; the act of making up one's mind. *The umpire's decision is final in a baseball game.*

de lib er ate ly /di lib′ ər it lē/ *adv.* carefully planned. *The hikers deliberately avoided the unsafe trails in the woods.*

dense /dens/ *adj.* thick; tightly packed together. *The dense woods forced the hikers to walk slowly all day.*

de scend /di send′/ *v.* **descends, descending, descended. 1.** to move downward. *The travelers descended the mountain in a cable car.* **2.** to come from an ancestor. *My family descends from Spanish settlers in Texas.*

de struct ion /di struk′ shən/ *n.* the act of breaking or ruining. *Hurricanes often cause destruction in Florida.*

de vo tion /di vō′ shən/ *n.* strong attachment; love. *The dog stared at its owner with great devotion.*

di rec tor /di rek′ tər/ *n.* **1.** a person who is in charge of the actors and technical workers in the making of a movie, play, or television show. *The director told the actors when the movie would be made.* **2.** a person who controls. *The camp director told a story to the campers.*

dis ar ray /dis′ ə rā′/ *n.* a lack of order. *My brother always leaves his room in disarray.*

dis grace /dis grās′/ *n.* loss of honor or respect; shame. *The bank president resigned in disgrace after he was caught stealing money.*

dis turb /di stûrb/ *v.* **disturbs, disturbing, disturbed.** to bother. *I try not to disturb my brother when he is studying.*

di vi sion /di vizh′ ən/ *n.* disagreement; split. *The divisions between the American colonists and England led to a war.*

do nate /dō′ nāt/ *v.* **donates, donating, donated.** to give freely. *We donated our toys to other children.*

down town /doun′ toun′/ *n.* the business center or main part of a city. *My aunt takes me shopping downtown.*

droop /droop/ *v.* **droops, drooping, drooped.** to hang down weakly. *The leaves of my houseplant droop without water.*

du o /doo′ ō/ *n.* two people or things. *The comedy duo kept the audience laughing for an hour.*

E

ed u cate /ej′ ə kāt/ *v.* **educates, educated, educating. 1.** to teach or train. *There are good teachers at this school to educate our children.* **2.** to send to school. *The cost of educating children can be high.*

e ject /i jekt′/ *v.* **ejects, ejecting, ejected.** to force or throw out. *We were ejected from the theater for talking too loudly.*

e merge /i mûrj′/ *v.* **emerges, emerging, emerged.** to come out. *The deer emerged from the forest.*

en chant /en chant′/ *v.* **enchants, enchanting, enchanted.** to delight or charm. *We were enchanted by the beautiful ballet.*

en gi neer /en jə nir′/ *n.* a person trained to use science for practical things. *Some engineers design airplanes and other machines.*

/a/	at
/ā/	late
/â/	care
/ä/	father
/e/	set
/ē/	me
/i/	it
/ī/	kite
/o/	ox
/ō/	rose
/ô/	brought
	raw
/oi/	coin
/o͝o/	book
/o͞o/	too
/or/	form
/ou/	out
/u/	up
/yo͞o/	cube
/ûr/	turn
	germ
	learn
	firm
	work
/ə/	about
	chicken
	pencil
	cannon
	circus
/ch/	chair
/hw/	which
/ng/	ring
/sh/	shop
/th/	thin
/ᵺ/	there
/zh/	treasure

e qua tor /i kwā′ tər/ *n.* an imaginary line around the middle of Earth. *Canada and the United States are north of the equator.*

e ra /er′ ə/ *n.* a period of time in history. *We have traced our family tree back to the colonial era in America.*

es ti mate /es′ tə māt/ *v.* **estimates, estimating, estimated.** to make a good guess. *My father estimated that it would take us two hours to go to the country.* *n.* /es′ tə mit/ *The mechanic gave us an estimate for fixing the car.*

eve /ēv/ *n.* the evening before a special day. *New Year's Eve is a noisy holiday in many parts of the world.*

ev er last ing /ev ər las′ ting/ *adj.* lasting forever. *The everlasting beauty of fine art is preserved in museums.*

ex pense /ek spens′/ *n.* cost; money spent to buy or do something. *My family tried to save money for the expense of our vacation.*

ex traor di nar y /ek stror′ də ner′ ē/ *adj.* very unusual or special; remarkable. *Mozart was a person of extraordinary musical talent.*

F

fa ble /fā′ bəl/ *n.* a short story that teaches a lesson. *Many fables have talking animals as characters in the stories.*

fad /fad/ *n.* a short-lived fashion or interest. *Bell-bottomed pants were a fad of the 1970s.*

faith ful ly /fāth′ fəl ē/ *adv.* loyally and devotedly. *My dog waits faithfully for me every afternoon.*

fa mous /fā′ məs/ *adj.* well-known by many. *A crowd of fans waited to see the famous singer arrive at the arena.*

fan ta sy /fan′ tə sē/ *n., pl.* **fantasies. 1.** make-believe; playful or wishful imagination. *His story about his adventures is pure fantasy.* **2.** a story with very strange people, places, or events. *My sister likes to read fantasies about lost worlds.*

fas ci nat ing /fas′ ə nā ting/ *adj.* very interesting. *Many fables tell fascinating stories.*

fee ble /fē′ bəl/ *adj.* weak. *I felt feeble after my illness.*

fer tile /fûr′ təl/ *adj.* **1.** growing and producing young. *Rabbits are very fertile animals.* **2.** able to easily produce abundant plants or crops. *The fertile soil of the Midwest produces plentiful crops of grain for the U.S. and other countries.*

fic tion /fik′ shən/ *n.* written works that tell a story or stories about made-up people and events. *Novels are works of fiction.*

fierce /firs/ *adj.* wild and very forceful. *The fierce storm blew down several trees.*

firm /fûrm/ *adj.* solid and strong. *The ground must be firm enough to hold the poles of a tent. My father told us to go to bed in a firm voice.*

flee /flē/ *v.* **flees, fleeing, fled.** to run away, as from danger. *The robbers fled from the police.*

fleet /flēt/ *n.* **1.** a group of ships under one command. *Columbus sailed a small fleet of ships to the New World.* **2.** a group of ships, cars, or airplanes. *A fleet of taxis waited for passengers at the airport.*

flex i ble /flek´ sə bəl/ *adj.* easily bent or changed. *Flexible muscles let you play sports and bend easily.*

for ma tion /for mā´ shən/ *n.* something made or formed. *Many rock formations in the desert were shaped by water and wind.*

for tu nate ly /for´ chə nit lē/ *adv.* luckily, happily. *Fortunately, there was no rain during the class picnic.*

foun da tion /foun dā´ shən/ *n.* **1.** the base or support on which a structure is built. *The foundation of a house can develop cracks over time.* **2.** the act of founding or bringing into being. *We are studying the foundations of society in our history class.*

frag ile /fraj´ əl/ *adj.* frail or needing special care; easily broken. *The fragile vase fell to the floor and shattered.*

frame /frām/ *n.* a structure that supports something; the bones of a building. *I bumped my knee on the metal frame of the big bed. v.* to express carefully. *Please frame your answer in the form of a question.*

frank /frangk/ *adj.* honest and outspoken. *My best friend is always very frank with me.*

fron tier /frun tir´/ *n.* the beginning of unsettled land. *Lewis and Clark explored the western frontier of the United States.*

fun ny bone /fun´ ē/ /bōn/ *n.* the part of the elbow that tingles when bumped. *I don't like the feeling that goes up my arm when I bump my funny bone.*

fur row /fûr´ ō/ *n.* a long rut made in the ground by a plow. *The farmer made furrows in the field to prepare the land for planting.*

G

gal lant /gal´ ənt/ *adj.* brave or noble; heroic. *The gallant knight fought bravely.*

gen er a tion /jen´ ə rā´ shən/ *n.* **1.** a group of people born about the same time. *One generation often does not understand the next.* **2.** the period of time between the birth of one generation and the next. *A generation is about thirty years.*

gen ius /jēn´ yəs/ *n., pl.* **geniuses. 1.** a gifted person. *Wolfgang Mozart was a famous composer and boy genius.* **2.** great ability to think or to invent or create things. *The way he solved that problem was a stroke of genius.*

/a/	at
/ā/	late
/â/	care
/ä/	father
/e/	set
/ē/	me
/i/	it
/ī/	kite
/o/	ox
/ō/	rose
/ô/	brought
	raw
/oi/	coin
/o͝o/	book
/o͞o/	too
/or/	form
/ou/	out
/u/	up
/yo͞o/	cube
/ûr/	turn
	germ
	learn
	firm
	work
/ə/	about
	chicken
	pencil
	cannon
	circus
/ch/	chair
/hw/	which
/ng/	ring
/sh/	shop
/th/	thin
/ᴛʜ/	there
/zh/	treasure

gla cier /glā′ shər/ *n.* a slowly moving ice mass. *Glaciers are formed by snow that does not melt.*

glit ter /glit′ ər/ *v.* **glitters, glittering, glittered.** to shine brightly. *The stars glittered in the sky above us that night.*

gloss y /glô′ sē/ *adj.* having a shiny surface. *We like our photographs to have a glossy finish.*

grasp /grasp/ *v.* **grasps, grasping, grasped. 1.** to take and firmly hold with the hand. *The tennis player grasped the racket in both hands for her backhand swing.* **2.** to understand the meaning of. *We had a hard time grasping the meaning of the poem that the teacher read in class.*

grav el /grav′ əl/ *n.* small rocks and pebbles. *Gravel is used for making roads and driveways.*

graze /grāz/ *v.* **grazes, grazing, grazed.** to feed on growing grass. *Cows grazed in the green meadow.*

grub by /grub′ ē/ *adj.* dirty and messy. *My hands were grubby after digging up weeds in the garden.*

H

half heart ed /haf′ här′ tid/ *adj.* without much interest. *I made a halfhearted attempt to clean my closet on Saturday morning.*

har mo ny /här′ mə nē/ *n., pl.* **harmonies. 1.** agreement. *My family believes in living in harmony.* **2.** a pleasing group of musical notes together. *Two voices together can sing different notes in harmony.*

harsh /härsh/ *adj.* **1.** rough or unpleasant. *The old blanket felt harsh against my skin.* **2.** cruel or severe. *My mother's harsh words let me know that she was displeased with my actions.*

head quar ters /hed′ kwor′ tərz/ *n.* a place where the leaders are; a main office or center of operations. *The company's headquarters are in Atlanta, Georgia.*

he ro ic /hi rō′ ik/ *adj.* very brave and honorable. *Firefighters make heroic rescues every day.*

high lights /hī′ līts/ *pl. n.* the most important parts of something. *Catching a fish and then showing it to my mother were the highlights of the fishing trip.*

hoist /hoist/ *v.* **hoists, hoisting, hoisted.** to pull or lift up; to raise. *The truck driver hoisted the boxes onto the loading ramp.*

hos tile /hos′ təl/ *adj.* unfriendly; showing hate. *After the fight, the students gave each other hostile looks.*

hour ly /our′ lē/ *adj.* happening once every sixty minutes. *The weather is reported hourly on this television channel.*

hum ble /hum′ bəl/ *adj.* not proud. *A humble person is gentle and has a kind manner.*

I

ig nore /ig nor ′/ *v.* **ignores, ignoring, ignored.** to pay no attention to. *I try to ignore the silly tricks of my younger sister.*

im mi grant /im′ i grənt/ *n.* a person coming to live in a new country. *Until 1954, immigrants coming to the United States were registered at Ellis Island in New York.*

in di cate /in′ di kāt′/ *v.* **indicates, indicating, indicated. 1.** to point out. *The park guide indicated the best place for us to park our motor home.* **2.** to show or be a sign of. *The weather map indicates that a thunderstorm is approaching the city.*

in flate /in flāt′/ *v.* **inflates, inflating, inflated.** to fill with air. *We used a small pump to inflate the bicycle tires.*

in spect /in spekt′/ *v.* **inspects, inspecting, inspected.** to look at closely and carefully. *My mother inspected the vegetable garden before she picked tomatoes.*

in tel li gence /in tel′ i jəns/ *n.* the ability to think, learn, and understand. *Albert Einstein was a person of high intelligence.*

in ter ac tion /in′ tə rak′ shən/ *n.* action between two people. *The interaction between the monkeys and the people at the zoo was very funny.*

in vent /in vent′/ *v.* **invents, inventing, invested. 1.** to create; to make or think of for the first time. *Thomas Edison invented the phonograph in 1877.* **2.** to make up. *Don't invent an excuse for your absence.*

in vis i ble /in viz′ ə bəl/ *adj.* not able to be seen. *Oxygen and hydrogen are invisible gases.*

in volve ment /in volv′ mənt/ *n.* the act of joining in. *Her involvement in conservation efforts made her a favorite with voters.*

J

judge /juj/ *v.* **judges, judging, judged. 1.** to form an opinion. *Don't be too quick to judge other people.* **2.** to decide or settle. *To judge a contest means to decide who wins.* *n.* a person who decides on questions and disagreements in a court of law. *John Marshall was a famous judge.*

jun ior /joon′ yər/ *adj.* younger or lower in rank. *John F. Kennedy, Junior, was the son of President John F. Kennedy.*

K

keen /kēn/ *adj.* very strong. *My friend has a keen interest in rockets.*

knead /nēd/ *v.* **kneads, kneading, kneaded.** to mix and press together with the hands. *We must knead the dough before we bake it in the oven.*

/a/	at
/ā/	late
/â/	care
/ä/	father
/e/	set
/ē/	me
/i/	it
/ī/	kite
/o/	ox
/ō/	rose
/ô/	brought
	raw
/oi/	coin
/ŏŏ/	book
/ōō/	too
/or/	form
/ou/	out
/u/	up
/yōō/	cube
/ûr/	turn
	germ
	learn
	firm
	work
/ə/	about
	chicken
	pencil
	cannon
	circus
/ch/	chair
/hw/	which
/ng/	ring
/sh/	shop
/th/	thin
/th/	there
/zh/	treasure

L

late ly /lāt′ lē/ *adv.* not long ago. *I've been taking more notes lately.*

lat i tude /lat′ i tōōd/ *n.* distance measured on Earth's surface north or south. *Lines of latitude are shown on a map or globe.*

law yer /lô′ yər/ *n.* a person who has studied the law and can speak in court for another person. *A lawyer advises people who have broken the law.*

lean /lēn/ *adj.* thin. *Many basketball players are tall and lean. v.* to slant or bend. *We leaned against the tree while waiting for our mother.*

leg is late /lej′ is lāt′/ *v.* **legislates, legislating, legislated.** to make laws. *Congress may debate before they legislate and pass a new law to the president.*

lend /lend/ *v.* **lends, lending, lent.** to let someone borrow something for a while. *Would you please lend me your pencil?*

life like /līf′ līk′/ *adj.* resembling real life. *John Singer Sergeant painted very lifelike portraits of people.*

lit er a ture /lit′ ər ə chər/ *n.* writing such as plays, poems, and novels of lasting value. *My aunt teaches English literature at the local college.*

log /lôg/ *v.* **logs, logging, logged.** to write in a record book. *n. I saw the ship's captain logging the day's events in his journal. n.* a large piece of wood cut from the trunk of a tree. *Our cabin in the woods was built out of logs from nearby trees.*

log i cal /loj′ i kəl/ *adj.* **1.** making good sense. *It is logical to think that your friends will attend our party.* **2.** having to do or done by sound reasoning. *The teacher gave us a logical explanation for how planets formed.*

lon gi tude /lon ′ ji tōōd/ *n.* distance measured on Earth's surface east or west. *Lines of longitude are shown running from the north pole to the south pole on maps or globes.*

loy al /loi′ əl/ *adj.* having or showing strong or lasting affection and support. *The old friends were always loyal to each other.*

lunge /lunj/ *v.* **lunges, lunging, lunged.** to suddenly move forward. *The soccer player lunged to try to stop the goal.*

M

mag nif i cent /mag nif′ ə sənt/ *adj.* wonderful; very beautiful. *The French kings lived in magnificent palaces.*

main tain /mān tān′/ *v.* **maintains, maintaining, maintained. 1.** to care for. *City workers maintain the roads.* **2.** to continue to do or have; to keep. *It was hard for me to maintain my balance on the icy sidewalks.*

mam mals /mam′ əlz/ *pl. n.* animals that give birth to live young. *Blue whales are the largest mammals on Earth.*

max i mum /mak′ sə məm/ *adj.* the greatest possible. *The speed limit shows the maximum speed allowed on the roads.*

mead ow /med′ ō/ n. a piece of grassy land. *A herd of cows grazed peacefully in the meadow.*

me chan ic /mi kan′ ik/ n. one who fixes machines. *The mechanic knew exactly what was wrong with our car.*

men tal /men′ təl/ adj. having to do with or done by the mind. *Learning to read is an important stage of a child's mental development.*

mesa /mā′ sə/ n. a flat-topped hill. *There are steep mesas in the deserts of Mexico and the United States.*

might y /mī′ tē/ adj. great in power, size, or amount. *The Mississippi is a mighty river.*

mil i tar y /mil′ i ter′ ē/ n. armed forces. *The branches of the military include the army, the navy, and the air force.* adj. relating to the armed forces or soldiers. *My brother looked wonderful in his military uniform.*

mis er a ble /miz′ ər ə bəl/ adj. very unhappy. *Cleaning up my room made me miserable.*

mis giv ing /mis giv′ ing/ n. a feeling of doubt or worry. *I had misgivings about loaning my sister more money.*

misleading /mis lēd′ ing/ adj. causing a wrong idea. *We became lost after receiving misleading directions from someone.*

mis place /mis plās′/ v. **misplaces, misplacing, misplaced.** to put in a wrong place; to lose. *My mother misplaces her car keys at least once a month.*

mis shap en /mis shā′ pən/ adj. badly formed. *A misshapen mass of wax remained when the candle burned down.*

mod ern /mod′ ərn/ adj. of the present time or recent time. *The Internet is a modern development in the computer field.*

mold /mōld/ v. **molds, molding, molded.** to form or shape something. *My aunt molds clay into pretty pots.*

mo men tar i ly /mō′ mən ter′ ə lē/ adv. very soon; in a minute. *My grandmother will arrive momentarily.*

moss y /mô′ sē/ adj. covered with soft, small green plants. *The mossy bank of the river felt soft on my bare feet.*

murk y /mûr′ kē/ adj. dark and cloudy. *The heavy rains made the water in the river muddy and murky.*

mus cu lar /mus′ kyə lər/ adj. having strong muscles. *Lifting weights will give you muscular arms.*

mu tu al /mū′ choo əl/ adj. **1.** something shared. *My friend and I share a mutual interest in insects.* **2.** having the same connection to each other. *Alexander Hamilton and Aaron Burr were mutual enemies.*

/a/	at
/ā/	late
/â/	care
/ä/	father
/e/	set
/ē/	me
/i/	it
/ī/	kite
/o/	ox
/ō/	rose
/ô/	brought
	raw
/oi/	coin
/o͝o/	book
/o͞o/	too
/or/	form
/ou/	out
/u/	up
/yo͞o/	cube
/ûr/	turn
	germ
	learn
	firm
	work
/ə/	about
	chicken
	pencil
	cannon
	circus
/ch/	chair
/hw/	which
/ng/	ring
/sh/	shop
/th/	thin
/th̶/	there
/zh/	treasure

N

ne go ti ate /ni gō′ shē āt′/ *v.* **negotiates, negotiating, negotiated.** to discuss to try to reach agreement. *The pilots negotiated an agreement with the airlines.*

net work /net′ wûrk′/ *n.* a system with connected parts. *The network of highways in the United States covers more than 400,000 miles.*

neu tral /nōō′ trəl/ *adj.* not taking or belonging to either side in a disagreement. *During the war, many people fled to a neutral country for safety.*

no ble /nō′ bəl/ *adj.* **1.** fair and honorable; good. *Knights were known for their noble deeds.* **2.** having high rank or title by birth. *Lafayette was a member of an ancient noble family.*

no where /nō′ hwâr/ *adj.* not any place. *My blue hat is nowhere to be found.*

nu mer ous /nōō′ mər əs/ *adj.* many; forming a large number. *There are numerous stars in the sky.*

O

ob ject /ob′ jikt/ *n.* something you can touch or see. *Any round object is a ball.* /əb jekt′/ *v.* **objects, objecting, objected.** to say no. *Does anyone object to watching this program?*

oc ca sion al /ə kā′ zhə nəl/ *adj.* happening once in awhile. *There is occasional flooding near the Mississippi River.*

off spring /ôf′ spring/ *n.* the young of a person, an animal, or a plant. *Our cat and her four offspring slept on a rug by the fireplace.*

old-fash ioned /ōld′ fash′ ənd/ *adj.* **1.** keeping old ways and ideas. *My Italian grandparents are a little old-fashioned in their thinking.* **2.** no longer in fashion. *The actress wore an old-fashioned dress in the movie about the Civil War.*

o pen-mind ed /ō′ pən mīn′ did/ *adj.* ready to think about new ideas. *Good leaders are often open-minded and fair.*

op pose /ə pōz′/ *v.* **opposes, opposing, opposed.** to be against. *I opposed them in the argument.*

o ver come /ō vər kum′/ *v.* **overcome, overcoming, overcame.** to beat or conquer; to get the better of. *Do you think he will ever overcome his fear of the water?*

o zone /ō′ zōn/ *n.* a form of oxygen gas. *Ozone is a pale blue gas with a sharp odor.*

P

pane /pān/ *n.* a sheet of glass. *The front door of the house had a large pane of frosted glass in it.*

par a graph /par′ ə graf′/ *n.* a part of something written having more than one sentence. *The sentences in a paragraph relate to the same subject or idea.*

par tial ly /pär′ shə lē/ *adv.* not completely finished. *The new house was only partially finished by spring.*

pause /pôz/ *n.* a short rest. *After a pause, the pianist played another piece.* *v.* **pauses, pausing, paused.** to stop for a short while. *The climbers paused at the top of the mountain to admire the view.*

pen in su la /pə nin′ sə lə/ *n.* land with water on three sides. *The southern part of the state of Florida is a peninsula.*

per mit /pûr′ mit/ *n.* order allowing an action. *You cannot park your car here without a parking permit.* *v.* /pər mit′/ **permits, permitting, permitted.** *Dumping trash in the street is not permitted.*

pe ti tion /pə tish′ ən/ *n.* a formal request to a leader. *After the people signed the petition, they sent it to the president.* *v.* **petitions, petitioning, petitioned.** *The community petitioned the city council for more sidewalks in the neighborhood.*

phar ma cist /fär′mə sist/ *n.* a person whose job is to prepare medicines and give them to patients. *The pharmacist sold her the special medicine.*

pinch /pinch/ *n., pl.* **pinches.** **1.** a very small amount. *The recipe called for two pinches of salt.* **2.** a hardship. *They felt the pinch of the new taxes.*

v. **1.** to squeeze between two surfaces. *These tight shoes pinch my toes.* **2.** to be very careful with money. *My mom pinches pennies rather than spend money recklessly.*

pi o neer /pī ə nir′/ *n.* a person who is among the first to explore or settle a region. *The pioneers explored the new country.*

plas tic /plas′ tik/ *n.* a human-made, bendable material. *Plastic is molded or shaped into dishes, glasses, and other objects when it is soft.*

plat form /plat′ form′/ *n.* a flat, raised surface or floor. *A large crowd waited on the platform for the morning train to the city.*

pol lute /pə lōōt′/ *v.* **pollutes, polluting, polluted.** to make dirty. *Waste and trash from the factory have polluted the nearby river.*

pre cau tion /pri kô′ shən/ *n.* care taken beforehand to prevent harm or danger. *Crossing streets only at crosswalks is a good precaution to take.*

pre cede /pri sēd ′/ *v.* **precedes, preceding, preceded.** to come before. *The letter* d *precedes the letter* e *in alphabetical order.*

pre cious /presh′ əs/ *adj.* valuable; dear. *Your friendship is precious to me.*

/a/	at
/ā/	late
/â/	care
/ä/	father
/e/	set
/ē/	me
/i/	it
/ī/	kite
/o/	ox
/ō/	rose
/ô/	brought
	raw
/oi/	coin
/o͝o/	book
/o͞o/	too
/or/	form
/ou/	out
/u/	up
/yo͞o/	cube
/ûr/	turn
	germ
	learn
	firm
	work
/ə/	about
	chicken
	pencil
	cannon
	circus
/ch/	chair
/hw/	which
/ng/	ring
/sh/	shop
/th/	thin
/th̸/	there
/zh/	treasure

pre cise ly /pri sīs′ lē/ *adv.* perfectly or exactly. *Please place the flowers precisely in the middle of the table.*

pre his tor ic /prē′ his tor′ ik/ *adj.* happening before history was written. *Dinosaurs were prehistoric animals.*

pre ma ture /prē mə chŏor′/ *adj.* coming before the right time; happening too soon. *I think having a victory party before the game's end would be premature.*

pre serve /pri zûrv′/ *v.* **preserves, preserving, preserved.** to make something last. *The city project will preserve historic downtown buildings.*

prim i tive /prim′ i tiv/ *adj.* relating to an early or a first stage of development. *Primitive people made tools out of stone.*

prof it /prof′ it/ *n.* **1.** money or anything that is gained by doing something. *Our profit from summer classes was a head start on the next school year.* **2.** the money left after all business expenses have been paid. *We made $10 profit from selling lemonade on our street corner.* *v.* **profits, profited.** to gain in some way. *I profited from joining the reading club by making new friends.*

prompt ly /prompt′ lē/ *adv.* quickly. *The concert will start promptly.*

pros pec tor /pros′ pek tər/ *n.* a person who explores for gold or other minerals. *In 1849, many prospectors came to California in search of gold.*

R

ra vine /rə vēn′/ *n.* a deep narrow valley, especially one worn by running water. *They walked along the river at the bottom of the ravine.*

re al ize /rē′ ə līz/ *v.* **realizes, realizing, realized.** to know; to understand completely. *I didn't realize how much I would enjoy this author's books.*

rea son a ble /rē′ zə nə bəl/ *adj.* **1.** having good sense. *Reasonable people don't jump to conclusions.* **2.** fair or just. *That is a reasonable explanation of what happened.*

re cy cle /rē sī′ kəl/ *v.* **recycles, recycling, recycled.** to make ready to use again. *To preserve trees, recycle your newspapers and other papers.*

re gard /ri gärd′/ *n.* respect or kind feeling. *She shows no regard for the feelings of other people.* *v.* to look upon. *I regard him as my best friend.*

re lapse /rē′ laps/ *n.* a slipping back to an earlier state. *Not resting when you are sick could bring on a relapse of an illness.*

re lease /ri lēs′/ *v.* **releases, releasing, released. 1.** to set free. *Children and dogs can release some of their energy by running in the park.* **2.** to permit something to be seen or published. *The next movie will be released in June.*

re li a ble /ri lī′ ə bəl/ *adj.* able to be trusted. *A reliable worker shows up on time every day.*

re peal /ri pēl'/ *v.* **repeals, repealing, repealed.** to cancel or withdraw formally or officially; revoke. *They repealed the law. n.* the act of repealing. *The government announced the repeal of the constitutional amendment.*

rep tiles /rep' tīlz'/ *pl. n.* egg-laying animals with dry, scaly skin. *My turtle Tama is a reptile.*

res cue /res' kū/ *v.* **rescues, rescuing, rescued.** to save from danger or set free. *Two sea otters were rescued from the polluted bay. n.* the act of rescuing. *Many rescues at sea are carried out by the coast guard.*

res i dent /rez' i dənt/ *n.* one who lives in a certain place. *Residents of the United States enjoy many personal freedoms.*

re sist /ri zist'/ *v.* **resists, resisting, resisted. 1.** to not give in to. *I couldn't resist laughing at my brother's jokes.* **2.** to oppose or refuse. *My cat resisted all efforts to get him out of the tree.*

re spond /ri spond'/ *v.* **responds, responding, responded.** to give an answer or a reaction. *The student responded to the teacher's question.*

re store /ri stor'/ *v.* **restores, restoring, restored. 1.** to bring back to the original state. *The famous painting* has been carefully restored. **2.** to bring back; to establish again. *The teacher restored order in the classroom.* **3.** to give back or put back. *The police restored the car to its owner.*

re un ion /rē ūn' yən/ *n.* a gathering of people after a long time. *Our first family reunion will be held this summer.*

ri fle /rī' fəl/ *v.* **rifles, rifling, rifled.** to search through and rob. *The thieves rifled the house in search of cash.*

roam /rōm/ *v.* **roams, roaming, roamed.** to wander; to move around without any particular purpose. *We roamed through the countryside all afternoon.*

rum ple /rum' pəl/ *v.* **rumples, rumpling, rumpled.** to mess up by wrinkling. *He rumpled the paper before he threw it away.*

rus tle /rus' əl/ *v.* **rustles, rustling, rustled.** to make a series of soft, fluttering sounds, like the sound of papers or leaves being rubbed together. *The leaves rustle in the breeze.*

S

scale /skāl/ *n.* a tool that weighs things. *A scale works by balancing the object to be weighed against the force of a spring.*

/a/	at
/ā/	late
/â/	care
/ä/	father
/e/	set
/ē/	me
/i/	it
/ī/	kite
/o/	ox
/ō/	rose
/ô/	brought
	raw
/oi/	coin
/o͝o/	book
/o͞o/	too
/or/	form
/ou/	out
/u/	up
/yo͞o/	cube
/ûr/	turn
	germ
	learn
	firm
	work
/ə/	about
	chicken
	pencil
	cannon
	circus
/ch/	chair
/hw/	which
/ng/	ring
/sh/	shop
/th/	thin
/ th̶/	there
/zh/	treasure

sched ule /skej′ ͞o͞oəl/ *n.* a plan of things to do. *Making a schedule will help you achieve your daily goals.* *v.* **schedules, scheduling, scheduled.** *We scheduled an appointment at the doctor's office.*

seize /sēz/ *v.* **seizes, seizing, seized.** **1.** to take suddenly. *The dog seized our tennis ball and ran down the street.* **2.** to capture. *The soldiers seized the seaside fort.*

sen ior /sēn′ yər/ *adj.* older or higher in rank. *A senior citizen is someone over 65 years of age.*

sen si tive /sen′ si tiv/ *adj.* **1.** aware of other's feelings. *Teachers should be sensitive to how their students feel.* **2.** weak or easily hurt. *Some people's eyes are very sensitive to bright light.*

se quence /sē′ kwəns/ *n.* the order of things. *In a sequence, one thing comes after another in a fixed order.*

se ries /sir′ ēz/ *n.* a number of events or things happening one after another. *A series of television programs about the oceans of the world begins tonight.*

set tle /set′ əl/ *v.* **settles, settling, settled. 1.** to decide on. *Mother always helps us settle an argument.* **2.** to order or quiet. *Music usually settles my mind.* **3.** to set up a home. *Many people from Europe settled in the new American colonies.*

shal low /shal′ ō/ *adj.* not deep. *The water in the creek was very shallow.*

shat ter /shat′ ər/ *v.* **shatters, shattering, shattered.** to suddenly break into many pieces. *The windowpane shattered when a baseball went through it.*

shin gles /shing′ gəlz/ *pl. n.* thin, overlapping strips of wood or other material used for roofs. *Roof shingles are often made of asphalt like the blacktop on highways.*

si lo /sī′ lō/ *n.* a tall tower for storing grain. *Silos are round metal or concrete towers that store food for farm animals.*

slip per y /slip′ə rē/ *adj.* causing or likely to cause slipping or sliding. *A cold rain made the roads very slippery.*

some what /sum ′ hwut/ *adv.* to some degree. *We were somewhat surprised when it began to hail.*

spec tac u lar /spek tak′ yə lər/ *adj.* wonderful and amazing. *The view of Mt. Rushmore was spectacular.*

stale /stāl/ *adj.* **1.** no longer fresh. *We feed our stale bread to the birds.* **2.** not interesting. *The television show had too many stale jokes to keep our interest.*

stall /stôl/ *n.* an animal's room in a barn. *My summer job was to clean out the horses' stalls.*

sub merge /səb mûrj′/ *v.* **submerges, submerging, submerged.** to put under water. *We submerged ourselves in the pool to escape the heat of the day.*

sug ges tion /səg jes′ chən/ *n.* an idea that is offered. *He made a suggestion that we go for a long walk.*

suit a ble /s͞o͞o′ tə bəl/ *adj.* just right; fitting or proper. *The soil is suitable for growing crops.*

sum /sum/ *n.* **1.** the total of addition. *The sum of 4 plus 6 is 10.* **2.** an amount of money. *We were paid the sum of $20 to help our neighbors pack boxes for their move.*

sum mit /sum´ it/ *n.* the highest part. *The summit of the mountain was covered with snow.*

sup ply /sə plī´/ *n., pl.* **supplies.** something needed or ready for use. *We stocked up on supplies before our camping trip. v.* **supplies, supplying, supplied.** *The clerk in the store supplied us with enough boxes for our move.*

sur viv al /sər vī´ vəl/ *n.* the act of living. *Water is vital to the survival of all kinds of animals.*

swipe /swīp/ *v.* **swipes, swiping, swiped.** to hit with a sweeping motion. *Our cat swipes at anything we dangle in front of it.*

T ▬▬▬▬▬▬▬▬▬▬

tal ly /tal´ ē/ *v.* **tallies, tallying, tallied.** to keep count of something. *We tallied our expenses when we drove across the country. n.* an account or a record; a score. *Keep a tally of how many glasses of lemonade you sell.*

tav ern /tav´ ərn/ *n.* a small hotel or inn. *Taverns were popular places for travelers to stay in Colonial America.*

tax /taks/ *n., pl.* **taxes.** money paid to support government. *Our state taxes help build better highways. v.* **1.** to place a tax on. *Governments may tax people and businesses.* **2.** to put a strain on. *This math problem really taxes my brain.*

tem po rar y /tem´ pə rer´ ē/ *adj.* lasting for a short time. *My sister has a temporary job at the mall for the holiday season.*

term /tûrm/ *n.* **1.** period of time. *That senator has served seven terms in the Senate.* **2.** a word or phrase that has a certain meaning. *"Good morning" is a polite term of greeting.*

thought ful /thôt´ fəl/ *adj.* kind; thinking of others. *Reading to your younger sister is a thoughtful thing to do.*

threat ened /thret´ ənd/ *adj.* a form of **threaten.** likely to die off. *Thousands of acres of forest have become threatened by the summer wildfires.*

thrift y /thrif´ tē/ *adj.* very careful in the use and management of money; avoiding waste. *The thrifty girl saved her money.*

tim ber /tim´ bər/ *n.* wood for building things with; lumber. *We watched the builders carry the timber for our house.*

/a/	at
/ā/	late
/â/	care
/ä/	father
/e/	set
/ē/	me
/i/	it
/ī/	kite
/o/	ox
/ō/	rose
/ô/	brought
	raw
/oi/	coin
/o͝o/	book
/o͞o/	too
/or/	form
/ou/	out
/u/	up
/yo͞o/	cube
/ûr/	turn
	germ
	learn
	firm
	work
/ə/	about
	chicken
	pencil
	cannon
	circus
/ch/	chair
/hw/	which
/ng/	ring
/sh/	shop
/th/	thin
/ᵺ/	there
/zh/	treasure

tra di tions /trə dish′ ənz/ *pl. n.* beliefs handed down. *Family traditions make holidays memorable and fun.*

trag ic /traj′ ik/ *adj.* very sad or dreadful. *There was a tragic car accident on the highway last night.*

trans form /trans form′/ *v.* **transforms, transformed.** to change into something else. *In the story of "The Frog Prince," a frog is transformed into a prince.*

tri o /trē′ ō/ *n.* three people or things. *The musical trio played piano, violin, and cello.*

trop i cal /trop′ i kəl/ *adj.* very hot. *Rain falls almost every afternoon in tropical climates.*

twi light /twī′ līt′/ *n.* the time just after sunset. *At twilight the sky looks pink.*

U

un eas y /un ē′ zē/ *adj.* worried and uncomfortable. *I was uneasy about speaking in front of the entire school.*

un fa mil iar /un′ fə mil′ yər/ *adj.* **1.** strange, unknown. *An unfamiliar car pulled into the driveway.* **2.** not acquainted with. *That television show is unfamiliar to me.*

un fore seen /un′ for sēn′/ *adj.* not known beforehand; not expected. *The sudden rain was unforeseen.*

u nit /ū′ nit/ *n.* **1.** a single thing that is part of a larger group. *The apartment building had thirty apartments or units.* **2.** a fixed amount used as a standard measure. *A mile is a unit of distance.*

un plea sant /un plez′ ənt/ *adj.* not enjoyable; not nice. *I find any argument unpleasant.*

un u su al ly /un ū′ zhoo əl ē/ *adv.* not usually; rarely. *The noon sky is unusually dark.*

up right /up′ rīt/ *adj.* **1.** having a good and honest character. *We want an upright person as class president.* **2.** standing straight up. *Tall, upright columns supported the courthouse building.*

up-to-date /up′ tə dāt′/ *adj.* using or having the most recent facts or information. *Before our trip, we bought an up-to-date map of New England.*

V

vet er i nar i an /vet′ ər ə när′ ē ən/ *n.* an animal doctor. *Veterinarians study for years and receive licenses to treat dogs, cats, and other animals.*

W

wa ges /wā′ jəz/ *pl. n.* payments for work or services. *The factory workers receive their monthly wages on the last day of the month.*

waste /wāst/ *n.* **1.** unwanted material. *The river had become polluted from waste being dumped in it.* **2.** the act of wasting. *Please try to avoid the waste of water.* *v.* **wastes, wasting, wasted.** to use in a careless way. *We wasted our money on too much popcorn at the movies.*

wea ri ly /wir′ ə lē/ *adv.* in a tired way. *The tired hikers walked wearily home.*

will ing ly /wil′ ing lē/ *adv.* in a cheerful and ready way. *The students willingly helped to plan the surprise party for the teacher.*

A—F Word Bank

_____

_____

_____

_____

_____

_____

_____

_____

_____

_____

_____

_____

_____

_____

_____

_____

_____

G—M Word Bank

_____   _____

_____   _____

_____   _____

_____   _____

_____   _____

_____   _____

_____   _____

_____   _____

_____   _____

_____   _____

_____   _____

_____   _____

_____   _____

_____   _____

_____   _____

_____   _____

_____   _____

G—M Word Bank

N—S Word Bank

_____   _____

_____   _____

_____   _____

_____   _____

_____   _____

_____   _____

_____   _____

_____   _____

_____   _____

_____   _____

_____   _____

_____   _____

_____   _____

_____   _____

_____   _____

T—Z Word Bank